★

INTO RED STARLIGHT

★

LAND OF SUNLIGHT

Into
Red Starlight

★

Douglas W Thompson
Author of Rise and Build

Line drawings by
Paul Jefferies

LONDON
EDINBURGH HOUSE PRESS, 2 EATON GATE, S.W.1
1951

Set throughout
in Garamond,
made and printed
in Great Britain
by Parrett & Neves, Ltd.
Chatham

Contents

. . . Whereunto ye do well that ye take heed, as unto a lamp shining in a dark place, until the day dawn, and the day-star arise in your hearts.

THE twelve-pointed sun dips from the China skies and sets in the island fringe of the Yellow Sea. In its place the red star shines down upon China. To many Western people this is the end of a story. They believe they know all there is to know about the red star dominant and they do not like it. They certainly want no more. They always found it difficult to follow the changes on the China scene and the falling curtain is to them a relief. They close the chapter.

To the Christian it is different. Under the Dragon Throne, the Nationalist Sun or the Red Star, China, for him, is part of a familiar world. His friends are there. Changes in fortune for the Chinese people mean, for him, changes in the lives of people he likes. For others, the

China news may retreat to an inch single-column on the back pages of newspapers, but not for him.

He has invested part of himself in China during the last half-century. There are universities, medical schools, colleges, hospitals and churches which he has helped to build and staff. Up and down the country are the specialists in religion and the humanitarian sciences whom he has sent there. This change is his change.

From the days when the Western missionaries were lonely pioneers of new fashions of life, through many upheavals, sackings, lootings, burnings and revolts, he has continued in patience to give his aid. Schools destroyed have been rebuilt, missionaries retired have—if the Chinese Church wished it—been replaced. The desire, therefore, of the Christian is not simply to follow the lead of Western democratic politics and turn from China until the scene shifts once more, if ever it does. It is rather to ask, urgently, what now? Is this the final cataclysm? Have we travailed in vain? Is the investment of the past years a dead loss? If the curtain falls and China's Western connections are forcibly severed, is nothing left?

The answer to these Christian questions is in human lives: the lives of ordinary men and women, some of whom have already travelled Home, leaving their accomplishments in the characters of others who are still perilously alive. Never did the Christian world-movement intend that there should be any other answer. In their work there has been no urge to invade Chinese sovereignty or social alignment. It was all done simply to convey to Chinese minds and hearts an experience of

8

God known as an active Person in His unique Son, Jesus Christ. The Church believed that British life, or American, when lived in God's friendship, became better British life, or American; that Chinese life also is better Chinese life when lived in that same friendship. The buildings, the funds, the foreign agents, always have been nothing but the tools of a spiritual task. "My kingdom is not of this world, else would my servants fight," so spake the Lord Jesus to a representative of world power in His own hour of trial.

Red China, therefore, is as near to the Christian heart as was Imperial China or Nationalist China, for in it are the folk which the Gospel made. The trend of the new People's Democracy is to dispense with foreign missionary staff. The strong link of visits and furlough between the Western Church and the Chinese is reduced to the slenderest thread; yet, behind the curtain which drops over the Chinese seaboard there remains the company of those who share our way of life, life lived with God.

That little company of Chinese people assumes a new and crucial importance. All that has been done in the past, every project which is dear to the Christian heart because of its saving power, is in its keeping alone, without Western aid to ease the burden. Under the red starlight, groups of Christian people in the towns and villages will become, at last, that for which the first Christian pioneer prayed and worked—God's Chinese household.

There is only one answer to the question, what is going to happen to the Chinese Church now? It is, such things will happen as spring naturally from the faith and training already built into the members of that Church. The tools of the missionary enterprise are secondary; the primary thing is the quality of life which the average Christian takes into the red starlight.

The most urgent matter for the Western Christian, therefore, is to know the quality of these people whose destiny it is, unaided, to do a new thing for God. Who goes the starlit journey? Can we find out?

This book contains five portraits. They are written to be folded to the heart of Western Christianity as a soldier's time-battered picture of his wife is folded in his breast-pocket through the silent years of campaign. When there is no news of those to whom, in China, the Western Church has given second birth, these portraits are to be taken out and looked at, as the soldier looks on the worn print in the light of the bivouac fire. So was that face then; can it differ now? When garbled news of new temptations to recant the Faith filters into the daily press, these people will look serenely up and ask if we dare think ill of them.

The portraits deliberately cover two generations. Two of the persons encountered Chinese Communism in its days of struggle but did not live to see its triumph. Their work built people who are now the Chinese Church. They gave pattern to the lives of the young, bridging the years. They are Moses to the Joshua of the other three. The other three portraits are of persons who have moved into the starlight with the Nation and the Church. This is what they looked like before the sun set. These are the deeds they did while they could still be observed. If we take the first two lives as the base line and extend the lines of character and action which were seen in the open days, in the other three persons we can project those lines into the new world and chart the future of the Church. This is true prophecy of the genuine Old Testament variety.

Later in the book, China and the Church within it are depicted from the latest material available, and the lives of the persons portrayed are laid against that background. As the stories are fitted together and placed in the context of the new Church and Nation, it will be seen that a tremendous fact emerges.

On the other side of a sin-divided world, Christ will be found to have prepared for Himself an adequate means of self-expression to do His will in a Communist zone. It may be a shock to find the Church has an unfamiliar appearance, and a greater shock still to see It wear red clothes. Yet it will be clear that these things are but peculiarities of the strange starlight. It is Christ's Church which is there sure enough. Christian men and women in East and West, may take courage and bear each other up on the strong arms of prayer. The growth of the Church in history is safe in the Hand which grasps the seven stars. The God who made the rainbow does not fear the changing light.

This book, then, invites you to look upon Christian faces suffused by the red starlight and therefore grown a little unfamiliar. In looking, the Western eye may grow accustomed to this new thing and the Western heart may learn to love all over again.

What strange contours did the eyes of Jesus see in the faces of Mary and John under the black thunder-sky of Calvary? Whatever changes the lowering sky wrought in that moment, He said, "Woman, behold thy son!"

11

" Behold thy mother!" And we are told, from that hour that disciple took her into his own home. Can the Western Church fold the Chinese to its heart—even now? At least we know that the Christ, looking through the mists of death upon beloved faces which strained to see His blood-flecked brow in the gathering darkness, bade them look not on Himself but on each other. Did He know that very soon they would see in each other's eyes the blazing excitement of the Risen Glory? Of course He did—and turning their eyes upon each other, He turned them from the darkness to the dawn. So let Western and Chinese disciples look upon each other; it is the Lord's command, and in the dawn, still faithful both, we shall meet with Christ at the eucharistic Breakfast.

Heir

to the Centuries

IT is a strange trick played on history that the world's newest theory of social structure should come to rule Chinese towns, where the tools of the Middle Ages are still in daily use, where the city wall still matters, and where the goods of the twentieth century are laboriously hauled inland up the ancient waterways in junks with staring eyes. In, say, Middlesborough, Communism would seem natural; the town was not there when Wesley preached—but Shancheng!

There is no clang of mighty steel works there. There

are no great cranes to finger the sky nor do the hooters blare to release hurrying throngs of the 'proletariat.' The bustle is of a different kind. Though hundreds of miles from the sea, Shancheng is a port. Wooden coal barges, built for one trip and then broken up, drop down river to it from the hinterland of the province. The river-men tie them up at Shancheng and wait until the prices in the cities tempt them to sail away into the world of factories. Lumbering rafts of timber and bamboo also shoot the river rapids to rest awhile at Shancheng until the flood waters rise to carry them safely down. Junks, great and small, are hauled up river by naked, shouting men; or, catching a puff of wind to fill their ragged sails, tack up river in painful inches, bringing in the salt, foreign goods and passengers, transhipped into smaller craft here.

It is a place of outlandish tongues, stevedores, boatmen, lumber-jacks, ropemakers, boat-builders, chandlers and the rascals who prey on ships' people everywhere. Just a century ago it was a neat, walled city, similar to hundreds of others, but modern trade has leapt the walls, and now the city straggles up one side of the river for six miles, following every curve, bristling with jetties, prickly with masts. From end to end runs one stone-flagged street: six miles of tea-houses, warehouses, temples, guilds, shops and homes.

With a shrewd conservatism, the Administration remains within the old walled city. The church is as far upstream as the city goes. Round it live migrants who have come down with the river to open inns and shops in which the river people can speak their own local dialects and eat their local foods. That quarter of the town is a brawling place and the Shancheng people look askance upon it. It responds in truculence.

This modern town is rich enough to attract war-mongers, but so sprawled out as to be indefensible. Time and again the same manœuvre has taken place. An army has appeared on the far bank of the river, blockaded the outfall and sat tight. The roughs of the town have straightway begun a campaign of loot. The Administration has then closed the gates. Fire-raising would begin in one area—always when the fire-pumps were in another. The Chamber of Commerce would then send emissaries to the invader, who stated his price, which was levied from the members of the Chamber, and the army moved in to perform 'exercise rifle-butt' on the looters. Some quiet would be restored—but not too much. A great feast of congratulation to the victor would follow at which leading citizens preferred personal requests, and the adjutant dealt with minor fees for special services not contained in the general levy. Order would now be complete.

The good citizen closed his courtyard doors and kept as quiet as he could; nothing would tempt him into the streets. Even the Chamber of Commerce representative going from merchant to merchant bore a special flag and armband for protection, which the mob respected.

To rule the church in such a tumultuous place it would seem to be wise to station a minister, burly, strong and vigorous enough to be chaplain to Commandos or Long Range Desert Patrols. But the church in fact stationed sixty-eight year old Ko Tien-wu, heir to the centuries. Tall, thin, frail, his face scarred with the deep cicatrix of a mastoid operation which crippled his jaw, the few grey

15

hairs of his silky beard completed the portrait of a gentle Confucian scholar rather than that of a man to live in dockland in times of war.

In 1929 the town was chock-full of ragged rebel soldiery who were billeted everywhere—in temples, shops, homes, and the school, chapel and houses of the mission station. Sentries lounged with fixed bayonets on the great gate and troubled the women coming and going to service. They robbed the shopkeepers, bullied the school children, ripped up floor boards, made fires of house-shutters, fouled room after room with their filthy habits.

Every day, Mr Ko would leave his cramped quarters and tour his compound. The minister's slow steps would halt; he would lean on his cane and turn an aristocratic gaze on the sentry. From sandalled feet, past tattered trousers and greasy tunic, his eyes would travel up to the confused face. A veined hand would go out and touch the rusty bayonet on the corked muzzle of the rifle. The grey beard moved and from the crippled jaws, in staccato military Mandarin, the question shot " Are you a Chinese?" The sentry's head nodded ashamedly. The old man's eyes would travel back, down to the wriggling toes. " You evade the truth," his voice would go on, quietly, bitterly; "only a Japanese dwarf could achieve such filthiness." The guard would wince.

Until the end of that tour of guard-duty the sentry would be abashed and silent and the women of the church would pass through the gates without a single ugly word. Mr Ko would totter through the gateway, tapping the ground before him with his stick, and, chuckling inside himself, would give his foreign subordinate a sidelong wink.

In the old, incredible days when Chinese soldiers wore rich banner coats and firearms were novelties, Mr Ko had been a military student, who—to graduate— rode horseback down the tilting yard, loosed his flying arrows into straw butts, threw the war-mace and whirled the broadsword. In his youth he wore the silken tassel of ancient chivalry; in his age he pleaded with the Nationalist authorities to spare the life of a young man sentenced to stand before the firing squad for joining the Communist Party. His life bridged the centuries. He was the living witness of China's dramatic emergence—and of the Christian Faith's transforming power.

Changes occurred in him down the long years parallel with those which Christ wrought in the hard, persecuting aristocrat, Saul of Tarsus. The old character lines were not obliterated but adapted to the needs of Christ in his life. He remained to the end able to produce the hauteur and command of the military officer. The ancient chivalry in him never died away; it was knit up into the Christian man and used of God for His service.

The day of crisis on which the Government forces moved up to deal with the rebel forces at Shancheng began in novelty. Instead of rumour flying up the long street to herald the approaching army, a whistle tore the air and a shell exploded in the city and was followed by the rest of the salvo. This interested the old gentleman enormously. "Come! Let us go and see the bustle on the street," he said. That was that.

The guard in the Mission gate had already rolled up

17

its banner and departed, leaving behind a welter of straw and rubbish. On the street the work had already begun. Groups of soldiers and rowdies had broken down the shutters of the rice and wine stores and forced open the foreign goods shops. Like streams of ants, they hurried to and from the shops, laden with loot. They piled rickshaws high; they stooped beneath their loads; they cursed each other; they flung unwanted goods right and left. Here and there a policeman screamed abuse at the looters who paid not the slightest heed. Suddenly, through the confusion a spate of rebel soldiers belaboured its way, running for the open country. They were un-officered and disorderly. As Mr Ko observed, they were simply "one street full of ration-eaters".

Their numbers swelled rapidly, for the rattle of small-arms fire was now on the town-side of the river and growing nearer. The mob thinned out, the people fleeing, cursing the incoming army for its speed. Was there to be no decent interval for a man to loot? Soon only a sprinkling of boys was left at the work.

Mr Ko had the main gates closed and went to the foreign house from which he could see out across the open country behind the town. From this vantage point he could see the headlong retreat of the troops and the conquering force break through the thin line of the street, bringing its fire to bear on the enemy rabble. There was no fight, "duck-shooting" the old man called it.

A horrible stillness settled on the town. It was as though no one breathed. The main force was now moving in and the people knew it. They were waiting behind their barred doors, praying that they might not be

18

the first to encounter the victors. Someone had to be first. Shouts and a scream tore the air. The hungry sucking roar of fire sprang up. The old man pulled out his great turnip watch and held it close to his face. "Noon," he said; "the general will be in by two o'clock. We will go to congratulate him. Dress yourself well."

He descended to his own quarters, sipped a glass of tea flavoured with a chrysanthemum flower—for which he had a passion—lay back in his padded deck-chair and fell asleep.

He was immaculate in his long silk gown, jet-black waistcoat and crowning ceremonial hat of fur, when with his colleague he opened the Mission gate at two o'clock. Across the road, a knot of men stood in a shop doorway and jeered at the spectacle of the two ministers. "There goes the foreign demon and his father, the devil, to make their peace!" yelled one man, earning the laugh he coveted. No splintering retort shot from Mr Ko's tight lips; he appeared to be afflicted with a sudden deafness; his silence was frightening.

Four miles of excited people were before them. As far as the eye could see, there was not a sentry, but the doorways were filled with peering folk. The ministers walked slowly down the street, arm in arm. As they drew away from the group which had first shouted, the old man hobbled along quietly. The next knot in the crowd, however, broke into a chant, "Kill the foreign devil! Kill the Chinese traitor!" The chant swelled and grew as they neared the group. The crowd, baulked of its loot, was out to recoup itself in amusement. A stone, flung by an hysterical lad, whizzed past the old man's face.

19

Mr. Ko began a monologue. Leaning his head almost on his colleague's shoulder—in calculated intimacy—he told stories of the manners and customs of ancient China. His voice rose and fell in gentle cadences. The crowd did not exist.

One stone breeds another and one jeer two. Catcalls, throwings, taunts, met them in waves as they proceeded down the street's twisting length. The hand which gripped the foreigner's arm never slackened nor did the voice cease its casual dissertation. A peculiar sense of remoteness gripped the young foreigner. He could almost believe he was in truth walking the formal paths of an ancient Chinese garden.

The journey ended at the magistrate's hall where a long queue of gentry awaited interviews. Here there were soldiers in plenty, armed and haughty. As he turned between the two stone lions which guarded the gate, the old man changed. The suave philosopher of the raging streets disappeared. In his place was an erect figure who merely lifted the knob of his cane in salute to a junior officer who was listing the general's suppliants.

"Ten thousand congratulations, captain," Mr Ko began. "The hour of victory is an hour of business." The stripling lieutenant looked at him closely, hearing his tone rather than his words. "Yet," the old man went on, "it would be highly unseemly if the only Englishman in the town were kept to wait with the other folk. You agree, of course."

The missionary now saw the role he was cast to play. He remembered some other words of Mr Ko's uttered on an occasion when a team was to preach in the open air.

"You shall speak first," he had said, "as a circus first displays its elephant. We will enlarge on your words, for our appearance is as common as our tongues." He had not said that the missionary's appearance was as rare as his Chinese.

The officer hurried into the inner court and came out to beckon the pair into the great one's presence. The general, flushed with victory, stood up to address the foreigner, but Mr Ko neatly intercepted him. "Your honour," he said, "his words are few and halting and not fit to express our delight at your victory or to state our thanks to you for driving off those blackguards. A great light shines on Shancheng this day."

The general cocked his ear at the sound of the clipped military Mandarin speech. "His wise friend makes up for his lack of words," he replied courteously. "Nevertheless, I will hear for myself."

The foreign minister took up the tale and asked with the best choice of words he could command for the release of the church buildings from ruinous billeting. The general's face broke into a grin and he turned twinkling eyes to Mr Ko. The old man stood firm. "Our foreign friend speaks like one born in Hankow, old war lord." He placed a hand on the old man's shoulder. "What an old rogue you are!" Mr Ko coughed and fingered his wisp of beard.

The general turned, rapped on the table with the butt-end of a pistol to summon to his side a hefty northern Chinese officer. "Out of respect for foreign relations, I would have granted your request," he said to Mr Ko,

" but because of your beautiful strategy, old comrade, I shall send my adjutant himself to see that all is done immediately." With amazing modernity, Mr Ko stretched out his hand in Western fashion and the general clasped it. The modern soldier prides himself on his foreign ways.

Outside the yamen the adjutant seized upon a rickshaw-puller without any more ado. The old man sank happily into the rickshaw and flanked by the adjutant on one side, the missionary on the other, and a soldier behind, he headed homewards in triumphant procession. A change came over the crowd; women clapped their hands, boys tailed on behind and men shouted, " There goes the old 'un." The rickshaw-puller's grin matched his passenger's scorching commentary.

It was a Christian feature of Mr Ko's character that he held no rancour against anyone in the crowd which had so recently cursed him and his friend. His remarks as he drove through the streets were all in the best of humour. An observer watching him walk the street on his way down might have classified him with patrician Romans forced to walk through masses of stinking slaves; but it was not so. He simply accepted the people; no other words describe his outlook. He knew them without a single illusion through and through. He accepted the fact that they could stone him. He accepted the fact that in need they would kotow at his feet. They neither frightened him nor shocked him. They could please him.

One of the minor trials of life at Shancheng was the task of getting out of it, particularly in winter. It was in winter that the synod of the Church in the province took place, and the only way to get to it from Shancheng was to drop downstream in a sampan and board a tiny launch moored, because of low water, below the city. The launch was crowded to suffocation with people and their goods. It was filthy and verminous. There was one dark saloon fitted with shelves to lie on for '1st Class' passengers, and every inch of the deck and companion ways was crowded with '2nd Class' passengers. In the saloon men and women huddled together, spread out their bedding rolls, and in perpetual gloom, simply lay around until the journey ended, which could be a week later. To reach the galley to get hot water or, indeed, to move from any one place to another was a nightmare journey contested by wriggling figures every inch of the way.

The old man would spread forth his roll, remove his long gown, and lie down placidly to await the moment when the launch arrived. His serenity was the despair of his foreign fellow-travellers. If the person who lay at his feet began to thrust out exploratory limbs, trying to get more room, the old man's voice would pipe up. " Fellow-travellers," it would say, "the honoured guest at my feet has lain so long he is growing." In the laugh which followed, the wayward foot would withdraw.

When the middle of the day drew near and the acrid smell of burning cooking-fats filled the saloon from the deck-house above, and, joined to the tobacco-reek in the air, made breathing almost impossible, he would roll over towards his foreign colleagues and say, "It's better than being at home," or "You could travel England right through and never smell a smell like that." He would pretend to sniff up the smell adoringly and then fall to coughing. Food did not trouble him on such trips. He would have fasted all the way, though he greatly appreciated the attempts of the women missionaries to make him eat foreign tit-bits. He would try, in spite of his crippled jaw, to manage an English caramel toffee when the noise would rise even above the hum of the saloon.

Propped up against the wall of the saloon, he would pick out people for conversation: an old man, a frantic young mother, a tough-looking young man, and dangle his conversational baits under their noses until someone was hooked. Then with jokes, old sayings and questions, he would draw out their stories, until the whole saloon joined in. "My ticket included a meal each day," he would say. "Which small boy has eaten it? Fetch them here that I may feel their pot-bellies." A gale of laughter would sweep the cabin, for everyone knew the meal contract was almost always honoured in the breach.

He would give the tenderest thought to making the foreign ladies comfortable. The care he showed for women missionaries on all occasions was a feature of his life; he had a tremendous admiration for them. The men he expected to be tough enough to do anything; the hardy courage of the women stirred him to the end. It was two lonely women missionaries preaching in the open air services of a town in Northern China in which he was a soldier who first moved his heart toward Christianity.

Old women, too, had a constant place in his heart. He would listen to any widow pour out her tale of distress. On such occasions, he was disarmed of his critical attitude; Paul disappeared, Jesus emerged. He accepted their stories without any cross-examination or testing; it was as though he expected them to exaggerate their plight, or even lie to him. He made his judgment of their needs on his own observation of them; the exaggerations or untruths were simply, to him, part of the picture.

In this exercise of mercy his wife aided him. A sweet, round little woman, her heart was as soft as an infant's pillow. She always called him, at home or abroad, " The reverend and aged Mr Ko ". She chided him, nursed him, screened him from rogues, and shared his devotional life to the full. The relationship between the old couple was on an intrinsically Chinese Christian pattern. Mrs Ko ruled the household and yet she did not. Her dominant thought was ever that her husband, out of all the old band of contemporary preachers, had been set apart and ordained to the ministry. Her home was therefore always the minister's home. So it came about that, ruling her home, she was in turn ruled by his calling. He was the head of the house, but they were both its heart, and the idea of subordination seemed absurd.

In the years from 1928 to 1934 much of Mr Ko's work centred in his home. During the occupation of the compound by troops, the house was church, meeting-room and office. The teapot and dish of cakes or nuts on the table were the centre round which a busy ministry of reconciliation and counsel revolved. This was his greatest work in that period.

In earlier years he had wandered far and wide, preaching. He loved to tell the story of the first attack on Pingkiang. At that time the Hunan province was closed to missionary residence and he came with a team into the town from the north. The population was stirred by the

25

arrival of foreign preachers and mobbed them in the streets.

The official welcome was even less kindly. Mr Ko presented himself before the magistrate to ask for a place where the party might sleep. The magistrate was most unwilling to help, but had to do something about the passports the party carried. At length he ordered a runner to take them to a deserted house in East Street. They were awakened at dawn by the murmur of a growing crowd outside the rickety gate. The people became noisier every moment, until at last the sheer pressure of their numbers burst open the gate. Mr Ko rose. As he emerged into the dawn light of the courtyard, the crowd backed away, shrieking with fright. "They are there! They are still alive!" Right and left they fled, leaving the puzzled preacher standing in the gate.

One middle-aged man alone remained, nervous but courteous. "I had to stay to tell you," he said; "being strangers, and some of you from other lands, it is but honest." Mr Ko took him into the house. Seated on one of the preacher's pigskin travelling boxes, the man explained that the house was demon-ridden. Other people had died in it. The crowd had expected the magistrate's stratagem to succeed and had come early to see the dead foreigners.

Mr Ko would laugh triumphantly in telling of those years and say, "Have you been in the central church of the Pingkiang station? It is that haunted house." He never lost his love of such adventures, but hankered to the end for the untouched places.

When his seventieth birthday came round—a great day

of feasting in a Chinese life—he announced before the day that he would celebrate the occasion by preaching where none had preached before. Two days before the birthday, he called for a sedan chair and rode off. He went to a little roadside town on the great 'opium road' to the south and there preached to the crowd from a shop. He came back a week later, wearied out, but bubbling with joy.

Like St Paul, however, Mr Ko discovered that the simple thrill of virgin preaching is overlaid with cares and controversies as the Church grows up. From 1928 onwards to his death in 1935, most of his strength had to be given to the round of pastoral cares. The great anti-foreign movement which began in 1925 had swept the country. A Church which used a missionary staff could not but feel its impact. The cry of national independence caught up some church members and preachers. Some recanted their Faith and became Communists; some took over the church buildings to begin a national Christian sect, and the catholic nature of Christianity was threatened. Mr Ko and a few others like him met the storm in all its violence. Sharing all true hopes for China, they laboured to preserve the Church.

As the wave died down, Shancheng was found to be in a peculiar position. Its cosmopolitan nature made the 'hangover' more acute—anti-foreignism lingered—and four ex-preachers, all of them quite powerful men, were living in retirement, having left the service of the Church. Each of them had joined the Communist wing of the split Nationalist movement, been caught up in the purge, recanted Communism, and returned to his home, bruised

27

and bewildered, but resentful. Their influence ran like an undercurrent beneath the attempts to draw together the smitten Church. The preachers who could be stationed in the town were loyal but not greatly gifted men and could not compare for ability with the turbulent spirits who had left the work but remained on the scene. It was a difficult situation.

Mr Ko threw all his strength into healing the wounds and restoring the Body of Christ. The hauteur of his military ways, his being a Chinese minister, and his own personality, made him the man for the hour. He rested above the quarrels. He had a policy. It was to keep or regain the ex-preachers for Christ but to hold them back from office in the Church. They on their part realized their mistakes and would have come back into the work. This he resisted. The task he set himself was peculiarly Chinese, simply to hold these men and yet hold them off.

His foreign ministerial colleague found this delicate poise between condemnation and acceptance very difficult to maintain. On one occasion, at a service when the Chinese preacher was addressing a large congregation, including some outside people, one of the ex-preachers suddenly rose up and shouted "Don't listen to this small devil! His words are lies. If you want to hear true Christianity explained, follow me to my house." The preacher was stricken dumb, the Christian folk were scandalized, and the ex-preacher walked out of the church, followed by a gang of outside listeners who scented fun.

This was too much for the foreign minister. He went round to the ex-preacher's house and dealt faithfully with him. A complete breach was the result.

Mr Ko, of course, heard from the preacher who had been interrupted—and who completely concurred in his foreign friend's action—of the incident. In the privacy of his study, the old man told the missionary that he had behaved very justly but also very inappropriately. He ended his long lecture with an invitation to supper some ten days later.

On the day of the supper, the missionary, looking out of his study window, saw an amazing procession of persons entering the back door of Mr Ko's house: the preacher bearing a basket, two ex-preachers carrying parcels, and last but not least, the offending interrupter who was dangling on the end of a string a large chunk of pork.

The erring missionary was introduced to the man with whom he had quarrelled as though they had never met before—although he had at one time been taught the language by him. He was introduced to the other ex-preachers as nearly Chinese, and the party began. It assumed the full dignity and length of a true feast, course following course, each provided by a guest. Not a word was spoken of the incident in the church. The guests departed, and the missionary, with a smile, asked Mr Ko just what had been accomplished by this ritual, as nothing had been said about the matter of the interruption. "Nothing has been accomplished," the old man said, "but this happy meal lies between you and that sad occasion. Now we can each go into the other's house without embarrassment. That is all. It was a very good meal; I can hardly bend."

Such actions made up the pattern of those years of

29

reconstruction. He was as supple as a snake yet as uncorrupted in his ethical code as a saint. He negotiated, he schemed, he poured out courtesy, he flared into abrupt 'foreign' speech or action, his repertoire of technique seemed inexhaustible. Round him there grew up a network of unbroken social and personal relationships which became the spider's web which staunched the wounds of the Church. This man was indebted to him; that remembered a kindness; this pitied his age; another respected his status; all followed him in the Way. His frail body and declining powers were his potent weapons.

Towards the end his public duties slipped away. He ceased to preach, and would simply appoint himself to celebrate the Sacrament of Holy Communion, leaving the public worship and preaching to his men. He loved those moments. His personal preparation would occupy Mrs Ko and himself for days beforehand. When he began to recite the service—for his eyes were past reading—he laid aside the pure Mandarin and spoke the words of the service in the coarsest local patois of the very village he chanced to be visiting, determined that the most unlettered old woman present should follow the age-old drama.

There must be many who were then children, now grown to adult Church membership, who, when they close their eyes in church to pray in the name of Jesus, see no Galilean but rather, Ko Tien-wu, with the paten in his hand.

*Mother
in Israel*

YEAR after year day dawned in just the same way over the one street of Fei-tien-shih. Perhaps it had been just so for centuries. First came the false dawn, with its specious lightening of the sky which always deceived the cocks into crowing; then, after the darkening that heralds dawn, came the dawn itself, turning the black street and its silent, shuttered fronts into cold, forbidding outlines. The squeal of a pig roused for market followed, and coughs and bawled words broke into the empty street from the inn, where a haze of blue smoke began to rise from the roof-tiles. Within, travellers were stirring themselves for another day on the road.

A figure emerged from a shop-front and stretched up to pull down the shutters. It was that of a little woman who tottered on small feet, her head swathed in a blue cotton turban, her quilted jacket already buttoned tight against the morning chill.

Half the shutters down, revealing the shadowed depths of the shop, she re-entered her home and came back in a few moments with three smoking incense-sticks. She placed these carefully in the sockets on the door-posts and bowed reverently three times. Another day had begun in the life of Mrs Chen Tsung-jen. For years, second only to the inn-keeper's wife, she had been early to stir each morning. Hers had always been the second roof to dry by the heat of the stove; hers the first husband out on the street. She was mother to the most precious child in China—or thought she was.

On this particular morning, her hands trembled as she set the incense-sticks in the sockets. The even ways of her life were broken up by anxiety. Her eyes were on the curling smoke, but her heart was seeing a tattered pamphlet which lay on the table of the inner room behind the shop. It was to her a venemous, dangerous thing, ready to strike at her dearest possession.

Spiritually, her whole self was centred in her 'wonder-son', Tsung-yee (Goal of Desire), who had been born long after she had ceased to hope for children. The wonder that she possessed him, in a world where every summer swept away the numerous progeny of other women, never left her. It was for his sake that she began the day early, placating the gods. It was for his sake she had the shop open so soon that her husband could supply the first travellers with their needs. The gods were those who watched Tsung-yee, the shop the thing which fed him, and her husband himself was precious to her for this one great gift.

Life had been very good to her. The easy ways of the village shop made its background. Customers came to sit, to chat, to smoke, and brought the news of the wide world of roads. There was no fortune to be made, but there was enough money for a little food, simple clothes, and enough trade to weave the web of good neighbour-liness which bound their home to the folk of the street and the surrounding hamlets. Above all, there was always the child, at first propped up in the milk-churn-like baby-pen by the doorway, then crawling over the earthen floor, and later out in the street with the other children; but never far away.

Births, weddings and funerals in nearby homes had studded the days, offering opportunities to dress the child and show him off, crowned with his scarlet head-dress and guarded by a silver locket round his neck and amulets on his wrists. The tiny mirror sewn into his cap scared away demons and the locket had held his spirit fast. All had gone well—until now.

The new menace to the boy, against which no amulet was potent, was that pamphlet in the house, and it was a different matter. It was brought by her husband himself, he who had given her the child. Now her utter loyalty to her husband and her passion of motherhood stood tense in their first conflict. The ages of intuition which prepare the Chinese wife gave her no solution. The finger of the Sages pointed two ways: one must obey one's husband; one must be ready to die for one's child. Which way?

More than half her husband's heart was engaged in the same pursuit as hers; he, too, doted on the child. His masculine life, however, by convention, made him build out into the life of trade, council and social activity in the street and in the villages. Never a day passed but he fondled Tsung-yee; never a day came but the outside world demanded him. He would—in the early days—lift the child from his own knee to his wife's, and in the later days he would order the child inside to his mother while he attended to affairs. She was illiterate and relied on him quite contentedly to be her eyes for print and her guide in social life. He was a mild, kindly man who both read and wrote. His leadership never irked; it was simple and ordained.

It was that other side to her husband's life which had brought crisis to Mrs Chen Tsung-jen and broken up the happy idyll of her peaceful days. But for its wider contacts, she would have lived on quietly content to see Tsung-yee pass from playing temples with the other children in the street ("Bow deeply," she would cry, "the gods desire dignity, not haste") to apprenticeship. He would have gone into a trade and obedient marriage. Children would have been born, and so her own life would have fulfilled its cycle in tending the third generation.

It had happened otherwise. Her husband, off at the marriage feast of a distant cousin, met a Christian man. He listened to this strange person telling of his beliefs and customs through the interminable courses of the wedding feast. At first, he listened as a man might listen to anything said over the feast table, with curiosity, and lulled a little, perhaps, into tolerance of the bizarre by the mulled wine. As the feast wore on, one theme began to penetrate the story and control the hum of conversation, as the bumble bee, by its reiterated song, rules the summer day.

"There is but one God and He is the Venerable Father of Heaven." This was the note which sounded again and again. The strange man appeared to sit light to the gods; he might have been an atheist save that his whole talk was of religion. Religion, as he spoke of it, had in it freedom. That freedom in religion somehow centred in this one recurring sentence which he repeated as a simple man will repeat something on which his life hinges. "There is only one God and He is the Venerable Father of Heaven."

At last Mr Chen felt impelled to ask the challenging question, "How do you know there is but one God?" The man had produced a grubby pamphlet from his pocket. "It is all in here," he said. "The Venerable Father sent His only Son to tell us the truth. This book tells what His only Son did." It was the father of an only son whose hands took the little book greedily; he must read of a God who had an only son.

Read he did, in the weeks which followed. The book was *The Essentials of the Gospel,* and it told in brief, pointed sentences the truth about the unity of God and His revelation in Jesus Christ. It captivated Mr Chen immediately by making his life itself—shop, wife, home, son—so much simpler to understand. The vision of the unity of God stripped life down into a unity. He was restless until at last he set off along the hill-road to the nearest town, in search of a church and the other books of which the pamphlet spoke. He read St John's Gospel and was convinced. This must be the truth His joy and freedom attested the word.

It was not so with his wife, Tsung-jen. His joy was precisely her fear: his freedom was her bondage. To her ears, his every word was hurled at the gods in defiance and to the harm of their child. Yet, he said, the ancient gods were no gods. He dropped the old practices. The lunar months curled their way in the old rhythm, but he made no sacrifices. Daily, he said prayers to an unseen God and told her that this was sufficient for everything. How could she believe with a thousand different possibilities dogging Tsung-yee's footsteps? He said a God with an only Son would protect their only son. Why should He, she questioned. Even gods must look after their own. Tsung-jen was torn in two. She had let her husband interpret the world for her ever since her father ceased to do so. Now his feet led down paths which could only end in the displeasure of the spirits and so in catastrophe. She was sure she knew where catastrophe would strike. Yet the very best in her, and her own desire, called to her to follow her husband.

The early dawn was for her a last dawn and a first, and she was afraid. She had determined, out of sheer Confucian family ethics, to follow her husband and go that Sunday morning with him to the town in which the Christians worshipped. She lit her incense sticks for the last time. She knew that that protection, with many other things, must be gone, for he had read to her the books, and though her heart was embattled behind the secure ramparts of a million fears for her son, her mind could not but understand some of the meaning of this strange Faith. The arguments it employed were ineffectual against her defence, but the old religion drove her forward to the new. If this was not saving faith, yet the Divine Compassion understood.

The service in the plain chapel, to which she came after bumping in a barrow with Tsung-yee in her arms for many miles, puzzled her. There was nothing to hold the eye in religious contemplation. All that was done centred, or so she thought, in a speech about the vanity of belief in many gods: gods in whom she had believed all her life.

It was the gathering after the service which led her small feet another step down a road. Women of her own kind took her into a room filled with women and children. They received her kindly; they took her child between their knees, and he found himself quite at home with the other children, who touched his bangles and silver collar. Tsung-jen noticed that the other children wore no charms and yet were apparently well. She heard them recite in shy competition the prayers and hymns which their parents had taught them. For the first time she heard the phrases which, from her husband's, had frightened her, fall from children's lips.

> *Yes, there is but one God,*
> *He's our Father dear,*
> *Gives us food,*
> *Gives us clothes,*
> *Every kind of cheer.*

The words slipped as easily from infant tongues as

37

the folk-rhymes she herself had taught Tsung-yee. A tiny flicker of security spread itself in warmth in her heart. Returning home, she felt just a little happier. Tsung-yee was repeating fragments of what the other children had sung.

Visit followed visit as the weeks went by. On occasions, the people from the chapel came out to her house and held cottage meetings in the shop. She trembled as her husband stood up to tell of his newly-found doctrines to his own neighbours. She was surprised at his force of speech, and the band of Christians was delighted to discover that the new brother had a tender, winning gift of explanation. Tsung-yee loved these visits. His home became the centre of the street. The other children envied him. His father was constantly finding new rhymes to teach him. There were picture-cards of the deeds of Jesus which gave the lad popularity in the street. They were good days for Tsung-yee.

Tsung-jen touched this new life obediently, but with, as it were, numbed fingers. Her heart would move out to perform some little religious ceremony of the old pattern for herself, the child or her husband, and then stop. She would substitute its Christian equivalent, but it would work clumsily like an unaccustomed tool. Again and again, she longed to walk through the village and offer a chicken at the shrine to break the spell of this new life; only her wifely loyalty prevented her.

Bit by bit, so quietly she did not notice it, changes took place. Things began to fall into place. She grew used to the morning prayer with her husband reading from his sacred books; she missed it if a morning slipped by unblessed. Evening devotions, a neighbour or two with them, began to mean something. She caught herself breathing a prayer when the child was unwell. She found colour in the picture of Jesus hanging where the ancestral tablets had been. She was covered with confusion one day to hear herself add a word to a religious conversation going on in the shop. Christianity became the routine of the house as the old religious life had been. She followed on obediently, and in time—for the heart must rest somewhere—she began actively to seize the new ways. There were certain women who were Christians to whose conversation she looked forward all the week.

In the end, still without any clearly shining light in the heart, she submitted to baptism. On the same morning Tsung-yee was given baptism too. She became a Christian, but not one of the warmed heart. Rather, she followed with bandaged eyes through which only a suffused light fell upon her soul. Jesus was not ashamed to call her friend.

Two years rolled round in the new pattern of life which centred in the Christian shop. For Tsung-jen they were years of slowly-mounting confidence. The new pattern, at least, had not hurt her child. The lad prospered, no disease struck him; his mind leapt upon and devoured the many books his father brought from the church.

For Mr Chen they were years of swift development too. He employed his new gifts of speech and found among his neighbours some to share the Christian Way. A little circle of believers gathered to worship in the shop. So, by a turn of the wheel, Mrs Chen herself became the centre of another group of women who were feeling their way to Jesus, often just as diffidently as she. They, too, were following in the steps of their husbands.

The words of Christian devotion now sprang to her lips easily. "Thank God, I am well," she would say. She would lay her hand on the shoulder of the mother of a sick child and say, "Husband shall pray for him. God is all powerful. Fear no evil spirit; Jesus quells demons." The words were now part of her. But her eyes were not yet open.

The opening of the eyes only followed what to her seemed cataclysm. Her husband's success in the village determined his church to ask him to leave the shop and become a preacher at a church in town. He closed with the offer immediately, sold up his stocks, and, like Abram, went out not knowing whither the Spirit would lead. With him went Tsung-jen and Tsung-yee.

The new world at first stunned her. Long town streets and the strange home without its shop-front made her afraid. It was only the fact that her husband had committed them to the work that made her try hard to find a way through her new problems. To crown the strangeness of her life, young Tsung-yee, as soon as the family was settled, was sent off to the Mission day school to join its three hundred shouting girls and boys. He took to it with zest, but Tsung-jen felt that the empty house all day long fulfilled her bitterness. She now resorted to long prayers to her new God, praying for light, strength and guidance.

God answered her strangely. Tearing his way through the school lessons with ease and the speed of high intelligence, Tsung-yee made a most amazing discovery. His mother could not read. The fact simply confronted him suddenly; under its impact he squirmed and twisted in humiliation. He was stung to action.

With shy and stammering hesitancy, he offered aid to his mother. The offer came, perhaps, at the one time in her life when Tsung-jen could accept it. The noisy street outside, the tidy and spacious chapel of which she was custodian, the coming and going of literate women, the occasional visits of foreign women, and her loneliness, all combined to drive her in the middle of life to become her son's student and learn what she had always regarded as man's learning. In her own bedroom, when the place was stilled, there followed stealthy sessions of laborious study. With plodding slowness she followed on behind her mercurial son. At last she reached the point where she could spell a painful way through the short sentences of St Mark's Gospel. It was then that God dealt with her.

Jesus came to her by night. Mr Chen had been out preaching at a house in the town and came back very late, expecting to find his wife asleep in a silent house. He picked his way through the silent church, and as he neared the living rooms behind it he could see, in his own study, a glimmer of light. He turned into the study and there, her head on the pages of an open book, his wife sat weeping by the study table. The yellow light of the glass oil-lamp fell upon the fifteenth chapter of St Mark's Gospel as she raised her head.

" Oh, husband," she said, " often have I heard you preach about these things, but I never knew anything until now that my eyes can read it for themselves. How could they, how could they treat Him so?" Her tears flowed afresh.

He put his arm about her shoulders and drew her gently. "Come away and sleep, wife," he said. "It was for love of us He suffered so."

"No! No!" she answered. "I must read to the end— go you to bed." In silence he obeyed her, and her finger once again travelled slowly down the printed columns which told the end of an only Son. On those printed pages she put her fingers into the nail-prints and believed.

For years afterwards, in that same house and place, she went on doing the same things. It was, after all, very much like being the 'owner's wife' of the village shop, but the quality of her service was different. She gathered the folk who came, from wherever they came, and folded them in, in simple rural courtesy. Her teacups and ceremony pointed her husband's spoken words.

After that late-night encounter with Jesus in the written Word, she possessed, what is a rare thing in an elderly Chinese woman, a ringing laugh, full of rich mirth. It would peal out again and again through the day—a hall-mark of her inward certainty. Spiritually, she moved out from behind her husband to his side. This became more and more so as his health declined and one sickness followed another. She now revelled in Tsung-yee's education and followed his career with reverent wonder. She stilled the house for his studies; she dusted his books like sacred objects.

Things went well with Tsung-yee. His religious life developed in harmony with that of his parents, his mother's serenity being to him a constant fountain of strength. It was after his graduation as a teacher than Mr Chen passed on and left mother and son to companion each other for the rest of the journey. Tsung-yee married a quiet Christian girl and Tsung-jen went to live with them. The gift, which in earlier life had seemed to her the crown of life, became hers as Tsung-yee's children were born.

That experience, however, did not prove to be the highest moment of her life. Tsung-yee could not rest in teaching. There was too much of his father's faith and mother's joy in people in him. He offered for the ministry of his Church and was accepted into its ranks.

His mother's pride knew no bounds. To her this was the peak of all human endeavour and nothing could compare with it. The joy that filled her quite overcame every other feature in her life. As her declining years took away her grip of affairs, her mind wandered along its own highways, but this one thing retained its focus, her precious lad was in the tradition of Morrison and Hudson Taylor. He began where his father had ended.

His work during the bitter war years was filled with sorrow and exile; she went with him. She trekked back into the far west; she laughed her gay laugh in crowded trains and in refugee camps. A little fey, a little sad, wagging her head over a mad world, in much loving and in great praying, she turned the last pages of her simple history.

God had still one more thing in store for her. At the close of the war, Tsung-yee, because of his outstanding record of service, was chosen to be sent abroad for training to return to China to lead the staff which trained men for the ministry. The shop-keeper's wife, become mother in Israel, steeled her heart with a serene strength to make her final sacrifice which was at the same time her crowning glory. She received his first letters from far beyond the seas, gathered the glorious remnants of her life about her and went, triumphant, Home.

Does God think one life well used which rests like a foundation beneath another, which projects forward into wide and adventurous service? Tsung-jen's life in any case bridged the gulf between the narrow ignorance of a village street in Central China and the quadrangles of learning. Then God said "Well done". The life which God and she created runs out into the red starlight.

A Lantern in the Night

AT Shwin-ko the river has already carved its way through the mountains and is flowing in splendid width past round hills, when it meets the waters of a little tributary tumbling down on its left bank. The river sucks up this refresher and hurries on toward the Yangtze, but where the two join, a narrow spit of land juts out into the main stream. Man has seized and made this his own. On it sits Shwin-ko—"Mouth of the River". More than a village and less than a town, its buildings perch perilously over the waters. The main road follows the left bank of the river, then humps itself over the stream on an aged stone bridge, twists sharply right and becomes the street of Shwin-ko. Here it is so narrow that two barrows cannot pass each other and the eaves of the shops on either side almost touch. The high road ends in a square on the tip of the promontory. Stone steps lead down to the water's edge, from which a flat-bottomed boat carries passengers to the other side, where the high road begins again.

One side of the square is occupied by the local temple and on the opposite side stands the Christian church, which presents a brave façade to the square but is supported on stilts with their feet in the river at the rear. The open door of the church leads into the narrow worship hall, furnished with backless forms and with little natural light to cheer it because its side-walls are high wooden partitions running up two floors, screening the preacher's living-rooms. Behind these screens the rooms are tiny and even darker than the chapel. Nearest the street is the 'study' on one side of the entrance and a church-members' reading room on the other. These are the two best rooms in the house, for they have little paper-covered windows. The middle room on the left is almost entirely given over to a ladder leading to the upper floor, and that on the right is fitted with a table and stools for members to use for meals. The last room on the left is both the kitchen and a bedroom. The rooms are wooden-floored, and between the boards the mud of the river-bank can be seen twenty feet below.

In this place down through the years—when drought smote and the mud stank with rotting refuse, when floods came and the floors were awash—Pastor Tsun and his wife reared their six daughters. Perhaps the house reared them all. Its shape, its work, its position, with the poverty which was always theirs, stamped themselves into their lives. To bathe was to stand naked in the winds which swept up between the floor boards, to go to bed was to struggle up the ladder, gingerly guarding a flickering lamp. To study was to sit at a tiny table in the pool of light from the front window. Outside, the barrows wailed and the pigs squealed on their way down to the ferry. At feast times, the whole place throbbed with the music of the gongs and lutes at the temple across the square.

Every Sunday, long before service time, the rickety place was filled to suffocation with Christian men and women who had tramped in from the surrounding hamlets. In winter their muddy clogs churned up the earthen floors; in summer the men's bare backs stained the walls with perspiration. To Mrs Tsun, a shrivelled little lady always in pain from a slow cancer, it was all just a part of life. She mustered every cup, boiled kettle after kettle of water, and as the tea disappeared, talked ceaselessly with the women. Mr Tsun, a big, smiling man, bustled from place to place, circulating the water-pipe and passing tea.

But what of the girls? Eldest sister was pretty and, in spite of the lack of a dowry, got out into a little home of her own. The tinies turned somersaults on the floor or buzzed round among the guests, dodging mother. Thirteen-year-old sat in the corner of the kitchen bed and hung her head.

That left May-ying. Too old for a pose of shyness, too young for the gossip of the women, she was one all alone.

47

Of course there was no marriage dowry for her either, and unlike her sisters, she had no good looks to compensate for the lack. Her face was plain and heavy, her figure short and ungainly. Her eyes, like her father's, peered from behind thick lenses. Her voice, like her mother's, was unpleasing. Visiting missionaries often wondered what soul hid behind that unlovely exterior and what thoughts lay unshared behind the dutiful courtesies.

She was her father's daughter. Through the broken years of closed schools he had taught her, taking trouble, in the classical Chinese fashion, to make up to her in education for her lack of beauty and money. The story of China is graced with the stories of many such girls, and May-ying's father saw in her one more.

Pastor Tsun was a man of restless spirit, always ready to try new ways of caring for his people or of winning others. One of his interests was medicine. A padlocked cupboard in the study contained a motley selection of remedies, Chinese herbs and plasters jostling with Western drugs. He treated coughs and colds, boils and ulcers, daily, but Sunday was a veritable clinic day. Here May-ying was his right hand. She hovered round the cupboard on Sundays so assiduously that in the end she jockeyed him out of control and became mistress of the medicines.

The cupboard did the trick. One visitor dared to look behind the thick spectacles and peer into the mind they shielded. He trusted what he saw and the confident hands he observed washing wounds. When a clumsy body becomes adept at one task, he thought, it is a sign that the task is done with love. So May-ying's hand on the precious padlock opened for her much more than her father's medicine chest. She packed her few belongings, said good-bye to Shwin-ko, and went off down the great road into the world of professional women.

The hospital and nursing school engulfed her. They did more; they wrought a strange transformation on the impressions left on her life by the Shwin-ko days. Her home memories were changed into an intolerance of dirt, misery, sickness and isolation. Her mother became to her a symbol of bound and needy womanhood. Her father stood out as an ineffective and whimsical champion of the impossible. The sense of responsibility for her younger sisters was charged upon her conscience and purse.

Science pressed its wonders upon her in the nursing school; the whole place spoke to her a message of cleanliness, space and liberty. The doctor whom she served appeared to tower above ordinary men in exasperating genius which she adored. He opened blind eyes. He gave new noses to revenge-scarred faces. He put up new buildings, only to pull them down and build again. He planned things only to cancel them. He suddenly swept into action when nothing was planned. He was god!

The missionary, who was nursing superintendent and sister-tutor also, both puzzled and drew her. She was all the proprieties rolled into one code, yet at times she was outrageously indifferent to the most exacting Chinese proprieties. She demanded truth in every detail and probed down through her students' minds until she laid them bare. She melted into tears at stories which left her probationers untouched. She expected a selflessness which was quite absurd, but she got it. She resurrected from the forgotten and quite irrelevant foreign history books 'the lady of the lamp' with such daily persistency that May-ying found herself listening, when on night duty, for the tap of that dreadful foreign lady's stick to punctuate the rough breathing of the patients. Day or night, in class, ward or theatre, in relation to dress, friends, food and faith, the missionary's own life declared her belief that the nurse is heaven's greatest handiwork.

The hospital stood outside the wall of a fine old city with an illustrious past and a thriving present. The shops were full of magic and enchantment; there were cinemas; electric light gave glamour to the streets. Near the hospital a modern bus station sprawled across one of China's new high roads which hinted at far-distant destinations. The church was big and thriving, and on the other side of the town there was another church with a group of German missionaries whose customs taught May-ying to differentiate between nations, so that her world was no longer simply Chinese and foreign. May-ying's mind strained and stretched as she met this new world. Layer after layer of new ideas piled up upon the Shwin-ko foundations until that narrow neck of land bore a sky-scraper of experience.

Four wonderful years passed between the first whiff of ether and the solemn ceremony of 'capping'. More miracles than are contained in the Gospels had happened inside that sleek head upon which the superintendent placed the starched, square cap, symbol of graduation. Back in her home, May-ying had made a simple village girl's decision for Christ—who with such parents could fail to do so?—but what wonders had God wrought since that day!

May-ying was now a trained nurse and her hands trembled as she prepared the copy for her visiting card. She gave herself a new professional name and brushed in the words which made all the difference, 'Nursing Association of China'. She called herself Tsun Heng-en, Bounteous Mercy. Was it the intimate friend to friend Bible classes at the sister-tutor's house which gave her that idea? Was it the regular prayers day by day in the wards? It was everything: space, light, prayers, cinema, city, travel, profession. No one could hold up one mercy above the others and say that it had made the newly-capped nurse declare her Christian gratitude in her professional name. Even pride had a little to do with it, for the character 'heng' is elaborate and difficult, only a well educated person would dream of using it.

Her next step took her still farther out into the great world. In order to train for a diploma in midwifery, she went off to Hankow—China's Birmingham—and into a larger hospital. This city and its hospital were like the old training place seen through some gigantic magnifying glass. Here was not one doctor but a team of them. Here was not one superintendent-nurse-sister-tutor, but a large staff of foreign and Chinese nurses presided over by a famous nurse.

The warren-like slums of the city surrounded the hospital, and from these slums the sick and hurt poured in a ceaseless stream into the wards. There were people everywhere, noises everywhere; the day was one long pressure of a world that never receded and never was quiet. At first May-ying felt as though she had slipped back to the days after she left Shwin-ko, young, inexperienced and frightened. This feeling soon passed, for the foundations of her training were well laid and her own proficiency in the wards and labour rooms soon gave her back her desire to grasp the whole of this new life.

She breathed again and began to explore the sprawling city and its two neighbours—Hanyang, with its mills, and Wuchang, the centre of university traditions. Great business houses, both Chinese and foreign, foreign concessions with their many strange buildings, large multiple stores, wide streets rife with motor traffic and the clang of rickshaws, other great hospitals, the universities across the broad Yangtze, the hurrying life of the streets, the city churches—all stimulated her thirsting mind to a ravenous desire for experience.

Above all, she absorbed the spirit and outlook of her tutors and their medical colleagues. They became for her the standard of what emancipated and educated human nature should be. The year of training ended, and she added to her visiting card the words 'Graduate Midwife'.

By now the thirst for more knowledge and new places consumed her. Frequently, she stood on the bund by the great river and watched the people crowding into the boats. She scanned the dress and manners of every young woman who went up the gangway. Could she get down river to the centre of the nation, Nanking? Could she get into the Ministry of Health training school there and become a public health nurse? How she longed to! She knew she was capable. She knew that she could earn her way through.

Then the call came. It came from Shwin-ko—that place now of vague, unhappy memories. It came like a voice from the dead. Her father wrote that the little country hospital of the area in which Shwin-ko was one station had reopened under the joint auspices of the Mission and the Government. Its battered buildings were under repair. He had been commissioned, he wrote, to invite her to come back and serve in it.

A physical nausea swept over her. Go back to that remote hill country? Go back to villages, illiterate people, the stench of the river bank, and the untidy mess of the poverty line? Far better forge ahead, and when her salary reached the right stage, pull her whole family out of that world. Battle raged in her soul. She listened eagerly to other girls planning their futures. She crossed the river and gazed at the trains filling up with university students as the term ended. Her mind even crossed the seas. Had not other girls studied abroad? She refused to go back home.

Her father wrote again. Poring over his letter, she saw in it little defects of literary style and wondered however she could have looked up to him as her teacher. Nanking won. She went down to the Concession and found a ship going to Nanking. So she paid the fare thereof and went down into it to go to Nanking from the presence of the Lord.

In the crowded third-class saloon, herded with students, merchants, political aspirants, pedlars and military wives, she found no rest. Her decision brought no ease, no exultation. Again and again, she told herself there were but two steps more to fame and power. First the national centre, then abroad; after that she could see her parents and sisters happy. Was not that true filial piety? Her father's out-look was village bound. The battle swayed.

Before her mind the suppurating sores of the village people paraded themselves in silence. She recalled her father blithely talking of new science while he spread on the ulcers a disastrous vegetable compress. The creaking walls of the ship reminded her of the pigs and barrows bumping down the steps to the river-ferry. The past be-came alive with a frightening stereoscopic clarity. It hurt dreadfully.

At last, the figure of her first sister-tutor reared up in her mind, absurdly carrying Florence Nightingale's lamp. Here was one with magnificent qualifications, free of the world, yet spending a life with ignorant village girls. She remembered how she scolded the girls into cleanliness and responsibility. She remembered the halting words spoken in the Bible classes. She thought for the first time how hard, cramping, difficult, life must have been for that graduate of a fine English hospital.

May-ying reached Nanking only to stare at its raw new-ness with troubled eyes, read the telegram from her father which awaited her there, and buy a return ticket. So the ugly duckling came home and the great hills swallowed her towering ambitions.

In the little town and its half-destroyed hospital she became a country nurse. What did it cost her? A high salary, certainly; the thrill of travel and perhaps—for a profession is a dowry—a home and children. Our God is a God of recompense. He even tolerates our faulty standards and rewards us, at times, in the paltry coins which alone we value. May-ying speedily found that whereas 'down river' she had been a new graduate among many, here she was a very important person. She stood high and alone in her professional dignity. So God salved her hurt until the work had time to win her. That pride of place held her up while He brought to bear upon her the enthusiasm of other people for new, clean, healthy villages.

On village tours she went down again to Shwin-ko and into the hamlets beyond. She met the poverty, illiteracy and pain again, but they were not as she had seen them before. Her mind pushed out new tentacles to grasp them. Somehow, an old man's ulcerated legs, which had been horrible when a mystery, became different as her sense of technique and power to heal came to his aid and hers. She began to scold and harangue the patients even while she worked on them, just as her tutor had done years before.

A final stage in her growth of character began. It rejected nothing. It included all that the hygienic years had built into her of fastidious cleanliness and love of modernity, but it included too the old feelings from the girlhood days at home. She became ashamed of neither, but built up an amalgam. She pressed her mother to seek medical aid; she purged her father's cupboard of aged quack medicines; she plunged into the work of health teaching.

Entering a village home with the team to do the work, she swept and garnished the little space she occupied while there and poured out stories upon the young women in broad local dialect but with material from the great outside world. They looked up to her, but she did not look down on them, rather, she tugged at their minds to lift them to where she dwelt.

In the hospital itself, as the war closed in on the area, she became more and more the confidante of the missionary and the doctor. Day followed toilsome day of war casualties, bomb victims, and the ordinary round of sick people. Then, by the mad quirks of real life, the war brought to her remote work-place the world which she had longed for and forsaken. The people of the great cities trickled back into the market-town and the villages. They came back loathfully, as she had done, and found in her one who knew their world and this strange backwoods world, too. She found herself with a general's cultured wife as a patient and—strangest of all—the French wife of a high army officer, too. She treated them, gave them tea, and made round herself a circle of evacuees to whom she could talk of the world she had left and whom she could instruct in the ways of the countryside.

Nanking fell, place after place down river fell, the nation trekked, the public health service broke to pieces, and bit by bit the world she might have entered disappeared. As it collapsed under the steamroller of war, so her remote hospital and villages grew and grew in importance. At last the day came when the Chinese doctor resigned and left. In the same week, with another nurse and a non-medical missionary, she was in the theatre, attending to a badly wounded officer. One nurse anaesthetized him while the other probed for the bullet deep into his shoulder. May-ying grinned up at the missionary above her mask and the muffled words that came through it testified to one more person grown by

Bounteous Mercy into maturity. "We act as doctors today," she said. "You had better sign the operation register, for if I do I shall lose my nursing registration." She was silent a moment, then picking up a fresh instrument she added, "Who cares?"

Two days later the patient, with his arm high on an aeroplane splint, called to May-ying across the hospital compound, "Thank you, doctor." She turned and rent him, "Doctor!" she shouted. Never call me that again. I am *Tung chih*, Comrade."

She is somewhere in the starlight now, and where everyone is 'Comrade', she is putting what she meant that day into the meaning of that hard-worked title.

The Thorny One

THE path twisted through the trees and turned up a knoll to the wooden gate, wide open, where Mr Ming Ki-kwo stood smiling—all five feet of him—to welcome his guests.

At the foot of the knoll the hillside fell away in steep cliffs into the water; from the house there could be seen a wide sweep of river bending round a bluff a mile downstream on which a pagoda stood guarding the approaches to the town.

It was almost impossible, looking downstream, to

realize that a busy town lay just two miles from the house, for it was ringed in by trees and secluded from the roads by the hills and the river. It was the sort of place loved by China's ancient poets, a place of placid reflection and humming insects, a fitting setting for the wine bowl and dancing pen of Li-po, greatest of the poets. To Mr Ming it was a hide-out from the prying eyes of the world.

Here the little man had come to rest, and in his country garments and with his land-hardened hands, no one could have guessed that this tanned farmer knew Shanghai intimately and had swayed the life and destiny of hundreds of people. Like many another, he was 'in retirement'. A few trusted friends knew where to find him but he hoped the world forgot.

He ushered his guests into the courtyard which lay behind the welcoming gate and led them round tidy stacks of farming tools and past a thriving vine which climbed its frame to sprawl over the roof. They entered the guest-room. A door which led out of the room had a paper notice pasted on the lintel. 'Library' it said astonishingly.

Mr Ming's foreign guest stepped over and gazed into this 'Library' while Mr Ming watched him with a quizzical smile. It really was a library. "*Ko I ma?*" Mr Ming asked, his grin curling up one corner of his mouth. "Will it do?"

His visitor looked into his face. "*Liao pu teh,*" he said, "unparalleled." The study was indeed *liao pu teh* in its contrast with the world of Chinese farming. The guest crossed to the half-opened window and looked out between its paper panes to the courtyard. The grape vine domina-ted the scene but the outer walls were covered with healthy melon vines and in one corner of the yard was a rich compost pit. All the things he knew in other farms were there: each had a tidy, almost saucy, finish to it which was 'extra'. Preacher, factory-worker, agitator, farmer, scholar—what a man, he thought, is this Ming.

It was an occasion in the Ming household. The town's Christian preacher, the schoolmaster, one or two other leaders and the local missionary had been invited out to see Mr Ming and talk over with him his plans. Like many another feast this one had originated in a crisis. At a church meeting Mr Ming had been so critical of the methods of evangelism and the men who did the work that a storm had burst. Tempers had frayed to shreds; unhappy words had sprung from stung minds. Past deeds had been quoted accusingly, motives had been attributed. It was all very unpleasant but not so uncommon, either in the East or West. Fortunately the East has its feasts.

Mrs Ming joined the party, coming from her kitchen to do so. She had left elder daughter, she explained, to supervise the cooking and came herself to do the honours of the farmstead. She looked so young that no one could have guessed there were sons in the great business world down the river as well as the brood of smaller children growing up at home.

She talked easily with the men, as easily as she would have spoken with women, in clear and thoughtful words. It was only if one caught her off guard and saw her sweep an arm across her eyes, as though to brush away a mist, that one could catch a glimpse into the hectic past of danger and anxiety. The perilous years they had shared were never far from her thoughts: they filed through her mind as she waited for the feast to be served.

Their life together had begun in the Church. She had been a teacher in the pioneer days of mission girls' schools. He had been selected for training as a preacher by an early missionary, famed long after his death for his choice of brilliant, difficult men. In the theological school he had been a tireless seeker, whose studies constantly overflowed from the textbooks to the whole world of new translations of foreign books. Social writings, novels and plays drew him irresistibly. For him, Tolstoy, Ibsen and Rauschenbusch lit up Christianity.

The young preacher went out to work just as the Manchu Dynasty toppled and there were left the dust-clouds of a shattered world. Through the years which followed, dozens of exciting possibilities of westernizing, changing and healing Chinese society, flitted in and out of the murk like Jack-o-lanterns. Mr Ming laboured in the literacy movement, the anti-footbinding campaign and the anti-opium drives. He watched the ways of his missionary colleagues and borrowed from them things which he felt brought new, modern dignity to Chinese life. He was wonderfully happy in those days of unspoilt ideals.

That eager mind, however, also felt keenly and bitterly the thousand rebuffs which the period showered upon idealists. The fragmentation of the national movement, the manœuvring of the foreign powers and the humiliations which followed, thrust him down into the pit of depression. Even his churches sometimes tormented him: the people lay so heavy and unresponsive beneath his eager battle-cry. The more bogged down the revolution became the more he moved to the left in his thinking. It became popular to blame the ill-success of the national movement on the pressure of the foreign powers, and following this public lead, Mr. Ming became more and more critical of the foreign-linked Church.

Remnants of the old world of Chinese thought in his Chinese colleagues irritated him dreadfully. An early betrothal in a preacher's family, an instance of illiteracy among their womenfolk, or lack of hygiene in their homes, called from him trenchant criticisms which strained good relationships, even with men who truly loved him, to breaking point.

He could not learn that one man cannot lift the whole burden off the neck of an entire nation. He could not appreciate how the new Christians had their wonder and energy used up by their own spiritual liberation. He thought that from the moment of baptism they should move to attack the nation's sins and weaknesses.

When, in 1925, the second phase of revolution spread over the country, therefore, the wave of Communism which swept across Central China found in his a mind prepared; it seemed that the day of opportunity had dawned at last.

Mission staffs disappeared before the anti-foreign storm and left the Chinese Christian Church to itself. At the time, Mr Ming was in a key position in the place where he worked. He did not for a moment recant his Christianity or become unfaithful to it. He simply drew near to the Communist authority and pulled his Church along after him. He was sure these two things walked the same road and could agree.

Among the Christian people who drew back from public life there were just as many who were merely timorous as there were of those who were far-seeing or anti-Communist. To whichever category they belonged, they were no use to Mr Ming. He drove straight ahead, aligning the Church's life with the Communist world. He declared the foreign connections to be ended. He pronounced the Mission property to be expropriated to the control of the Chinese Christian committee which he set up. He spoke of the Church as a people's movement, democratic, non-imperialist and uncontrolled. Every step he took identified him more surely with the regime. Being virile and trained, he soon became a local leader in the new society with powers beyond the circle of Church life.

Then came the crash which the far-seeing had anticipated when they went quietly into the country and ceased to be noticed. The territory was regained for Nationalism, and Communism was outlawed. The ponderous machine of ' pacification' lumbered into action, and Communism and pro-Communists were hunted down. As heads rolled off under the sweep of the broadsword, Mr Ming's family crept into the country, and he burrowed into the safe anonymity of Shanghai. His name was posted; he was wanted. His wife and family would have done, for family blood could atone if the criminal himself could not be found. In Shanghai he found work in a factory and by and by his family joined him there. So they cheated the gallows.

Meanwhile, where Mr Ming had reigned for his brief period, the Church reformed itself under leaders who returned and carried on through the years of purge and anti-Communist war. His name was left unspoken. Within the Nationalist area the hunt went on. The pressure varied with the fortunes of battle; there were periods of quietness in which no one died; there were days when ten or twenty died together. At last, finding that severity made no gains, the Government changed its policy and tried to win the hearts of the hill-people by actual projects of social reconstruction. The Communist sympathizers were still under sentence of death, but there were constructive things done which gave light to the sombre picture.

Quietly Mr Ming moved back and set up home in his ancestral farmstead. Publicly he bore a new name, privately he was a reshaped person. The old restless urge to service was still in him as was the flaring criticism of corruption, but he now saw that a man's immediate circle is the one place in which he can do anything which really lasts. Shanghai's millions made him a farmer. One by one he took up the threads of the peasant's life and applied to them new thought. He kept contact with rural research centres; he taught his neighbours to read. He collected old folk-tunes and composed for them new songs for his family and neighbours to sing in the evenings. He married his books to the soil.

The way back into the local church was far from easy. People never spoke publicly of his return or of his past; none would have on his hands the blood of a brother. Yet all remembered the days that were gone, and some of the leaders wondered whether this powerful man would be content without a place of leadership.

The battered church began to regain strength and take part in the general drive of social service which the Government advertised as its policy for the ex-Communist areas. The Mission schoolmaster and others like him began work in the villages. It was the task of persuading the slower minds among the church members to join in this new way of service which precipitated the quarrel and led to the feast at Mr Ming's house which Mrs Ming had proposed.

The timorous souls in the general meeting had stolidly refused to attempt a new piece of work. Mr Ming had broken his silence, stood up and poured out a torrent of argument in support of the new project. It must have seemed strange to his hearers: what was this? Was this a first move toward re-instatement? What words were these from one who had appropriated church property? Human nature can stand much, but not this. The first words of retrospective criticism sent the meeting into an uproar.

As though to point the danger, that very day three young captured Communists, who had been taken wounded in a village foray, were shot like dogs at the Mission gate. A detachment of the 'Other Movements Investigation Brigade' (political police) had recently descended on the town and once more its population was being screened. Not a few persons were trembling in their homes and avoiding public places.

So because of turmoil and peril Mrs Ming once more made a feast to straighten things out. There were no signs of trembling in Ming Ki-kwo as the feast ended and the little group sat drinking tea in the library. With a gentle delicacy he opened up the discussion himself. The Church had many problems, he told them: there was the billeting of troops in our property, the reclamation of our school, the constant dislocation of war savaging the work in the villages. There were the ordinary things, such as training new members, and the extraordinary, of applying new methods. Let no one think that any desires for a job in Brother Ming's heart were to be added to its burdens.

The little man sleeked his hand across his hair. In some ways, he told them, his thoughts of 'that period' had not changed. The schoolmaster shuffled until a smile rebuked him. Some things he had thought, then, repeated Mr Ming, he was still sure, were right. The future of the Christian religion in China depended not on its paid staff, Chinese or foreign, but upon powerful, educated and socially responsible common people, especially upon good farmers. He no longer wished to be anything else but one who worked on the land and gave his work and his leisure to God.

His heart warmed to the vision he saw and his words rushed on with the old fire. He was sure that placed as he was, with his land under his feet and his books on the shelf, he could do as much and maybe more than he had ever done before in the service of the Church. He thought that in time the Christian people who were slow to move would listen more to him as he spoke to them than to others who did not till the land. He would reappear, he said, and preach each Sunday. He would take part in social campaigns. He would teach or work on committees. The school could stock its land from his seed-beds. Life was going to be good. Let the leaders' hearts rest and their stomachs digest in peace.

His friends looked deeply into two lambent eyes and believed.

"And the political police?" It was the hard voice of the schoolmaster which broke up the magic moment with brutal questions. "How many times can you stand on a public platform before they enquire into your history?"

Mr Ming flung up his right arm. "God knows," he said simply.

His wife leaned forward on her chair in the corner of the room. One hand gripped tightly on each knee so that their veins stood out like cords. "Honourable friends," she said, "Ki-kwo and I have talked this out in the nights. It is better to die than to refrain from the things which God says in the heart must be done. The matter is so." She picked up a flute. "Come, let us listen to the new song about mosquitoes which my husband has written for the Health Week. It talks of what folk would think if the mosquito were as big as a water buffalo."

And it was so. Within a week, Mr Ming was on the platform in town acting parodies of the people's unhygienic habits and superstitions while a vast audience roared with laughter to see its own faults portrayed. Security police clapped with the rest. As the months wore into years, he preached Sunday by Sunday and toured the villages with the teams. Farmers listening to him and seeing his hands and clothes nodded sage heads in sympathy. His broad local dialect, which he could produce at will, helped his hearers and screened him from the outlandish police. He bore a charmed life and came to no harm. "Every breath I draw is the world's newest miracle," he would declare.

His course ran on, filled with absorbing work and virile witness until the war reached out its fingers and the Japanese troops after bloody fighting at last pushed through the hills and occupied the town. The staff was moved into free China to work with the refugee people. Many Christians withdrew behind the Chinese guerilla line in the mountains. The church and preacher's house gaped empty and the shopkeepers and others who had to remain were left shepherdless. Mr Ming left his farmstead and moved into the church buildings. Part he used for a tiny business which screened his activities; the rest he used as a rallying centre. He was pastor unpaid and met the Japanese authority with an almost contemptuous ability. Nothing the clumsy 'Eastern foreigners' could invent could give a moment's anxiety to one who for years had evaded the vigilance of his own nation's Gestapo. He held the Church's life together until the enemy was thrown out and others could return; then, aged, he went back to his farm.

So to the starlight; could any other land cause a man's life to box the compass as China had spun the needle through three hundred and sixty degrees in the life of Mr Ming? Today he lives in a Communist world. The old fear should at last be lifted—logic would demand it— it is not. Since those days of Communist activity he has worked beside resurgent Nationalism and Japanese invaders. Now, if caught, he must pay for these phases, not receive applause for that red pioneering. He would ask every Christian in a changing world, how many types of collaborator must a man appear to be if he is a Christian determined to collaborate with God?

Heir

to the Future

THE missionary tramped the yard-wide slate track. A towering hill rose from his feet on the left hand and, bounded by precipitous slopes, the river flowed down on his right. He looked down into its sliding waters with regret for he was tired; it was the height of summer and he had already walked twenty miles. The end was so near and yet so far. On the farther side of the river he could identify the place he sought by the contour of the hills, but the waters rolled in between, deep, unfordable.

He must go downstream two more miles, cross the

wooden bridge and then return, scrambling over the hump of the hills to the hamlet. It was too bad. A terse saying of Mencius marched with his aching feet, " God, when about to use a man, will try his soul with bitterness, embitter his bones and sinews with toil, grip his body in hunger . . ."

A long, high call from across the river halted the flow of the quotation. " Hoooo! Hoooo! " It drifted over the river and echoed against the hills. He stopped and looked away across to the other shore. A youth stood there, naked but for his trousers which were rolled high up his thighs. The lad was waving his head-scarf vigorously above his head. " Stay where you are . . . can you hear me? I am coming . . . coming . . . stay where you are." The missionary raised both arms above his head and, waving them, called back, " I hear you." The echoes rebounded from hill to hill, " Hear . . hear . . . hear."

The lad on the far bank ran down the baked rocks like a goat and plunged into the water. He wrestled there for a moment and then stood up, as though on the face of the waters, poling his way swiftly in a skilled upstream diagonal. No craft could be seen and he looked like some scudding insect propelling itself by one mighty leg. Having made sufficient tideway, the lad turned and swept down with the current. Within a few seconds, the missionary saw lying below him at the water's edge three six-inch trunks of bamboo held loosely together with a twist of rope at either end. They made a raft perhaps twenty feet long. The boy stood neatly balanced on the slender end of his perilous craft, leaning on his pole, head cocked on one side, a thrilling study in bronze. " I waited to see you pass. Come down and save your legs," he called. The baggage coolie looked grimly down at the raft, "and wet your trousers," he added.

They worked their way gingerly down the steep bank of the river and directed by the boy, distributed themselves and their boxes along the length of the raft. The coolie was quite right, they sat awash in the green waters. The lad pushed off with confident dexterity and the raft slipped out into the stream once more. He was shy now and stammered as he bade the passengers sit still lest the three stems of bamboo should come apart. There was no stammer, however, in his arms. Left, right, left, left, right, the pole swept, throwing off cascades of jewelled drops and the crazy craft leapt gurgling home.

A little forethought, a patient wait, a kindly heart and much skill, these were the characteristics which saved tired legs a long trail and marked Way Sung-min's first recorded deed of service within the Church of Christ. They marked many a sterner task in the following years. He was but a farm lad then, tilling his people's sullen hill soil. He had just enough education to read a newspaper or puzzle over a Gospel, but was master of the hoe, the oar or the axe. Within, he was living in an excited dream born of the challenge of the new Faith which was sweeping his village. He believed that Christianity was bringing a new age to his homestead and he snuffed up every breath of change like the wild ass that none can turn away.

He was born in the year in which the Communist Party of China was founded and grew up in the strange, dislocated world of the nation's fight for law and order. The little hamlet in which every person bore his surname, had seen its share of the grim struggle for power. Its remote anchorage in the cleft of the hills had protected it from complete desolation; it survived, but its outlets to markets had been closed and Nationalist and Communist troops followed each other in billeting themselves in its houses. In its survival it was lamed and destitute.

After the Nationalist victories of the 1930s, when the countryside settled down to a period of armed peace, there remained in this place one aged Christian—a great uncle of Sung-min. The nearest church had been gutted and its membership scattered. There were many places in which one quiet believer was all that remained.

Things soon became different. A preacher scoured the valleys, seeking his ravaged flock, and under the Christian banner, a wide programme of reconstruction received a tumultuous welcome. Young men and women entered the Church in keen reaction from the wordy promises of the world, for in it they found actualities which responded to their needs and hopes—education, co-operative loans, home rebuilding and worship full of rural lore to tie all together. Attracted by the lodestone of the one old man, the Church came to Sung-min's hamlet too, and he with his shy young wife came in with the others.

He was the most 'rough and ready' of a group of four cousins who warmed to the message. One cousin was clever and soon found his way out of the village into a teacher-training school. One was an old-style doctor and found his task in adapting himself to the use of simple Western medicines. One was a farmer by vocation as well as breeding and discovered his place in organizing local co-operative societies. Sung-min was the gawky one, with knobbly knees and stiff black hair which swept up, untrained, over a face that looked ever surprised.

In the life of the little church, which in those days still worshipped in the ancestral hall, his contribution was a dog-like devotion to the preacher whose work covered the area and to the missionary who planned the work in the county. He was retriever to their hunter. Because of his thick local brogue and shy stammer he served with his legs and eager face. As circles of people sat round wood fires, listening to the preacher, he would crash into the conversation with a hurried, broken sentence and then fall silent when the folk all turned to look at him. That halting speech did more than rhetoric; it drew attention to his eager face. He was a good exhibit.

In this way his influence spread without anyone noting whose influence it really was. Remote places, locked in the hills, responded to his wanderings by producing young men who caught his infectious enthusiasm and laid their more facile talents at the service of the Church, often in teaching in night schools.

While his teacher-cousin's Christian contacts ran upwards out of the village, Sung-min's grew more and more down into the life of the peasantry. Two things, at last, began to overcome his shy inarticulateness—a new hymn-book and people's plays. He mastered the numerical notation of the new hymn-book and became an enthusiast for song. After worship in the ancestral hall or in a farm-house, he would plague the missionary by keeping the young men together until they had been introduced to six or seven hymns which had caught his fancy. The book contained some genuine Chinese lyrics set to Chinese tunes and the missionary noted that Sung-min had an untutored preference for these. It was when he noticed this that he began to wonder where this young man would end.

One of the hymns was an adaptation of a Communist warsong, *Workers of the world unite*. This was Sung-min's favourite, and his stammering tongue was loosed as he rent the midnight silence of the hills with its refrain:

> *Arise, arise, ye sinners of the world,*
> *Shoulder your Cross!*
> *Attack the evil spirits*
> *And follow in the footsteps of your Lord.*

His shyness also yielded when in a village play he was told to portray a sick person whose life was being ruined by superstition. He would plunge in with gusto. He would set the audience rocking with laughter. " Here goes my last chicken," he would shout, holding the squawking bird by its legs. " I shall offer it to the Goddess of Mercy for my wife's health—then I shall eat it. How hungry I am already . . . I shall add a little ginger to the gravy . . . O bliss . . . poor wife . . . good wife . . . she may have a little of the gravy . . . but not too much because of the ginger." Under the flaring paraffin lamp he exposed ruthlessly the mean little thoughts which so often go with beliefs in little gods.

In spite of his progress toward self-expression, it was a complete surprise when, the three cousins offering to study for the lay-preachers' examination course in their leisure, Sung-min offered too. The preacher in charge pondered long before he wrote down that name. Finally, he only did so because he thought that the lad in his wanderings

76

would be better off for a wider knowledge of the Bible and of theology.

The first school which Sung-min attended revealed a new angle on his religion. He mixed with young people from all over the country, and in the three weeks in which they lived together he gained the same influence over them as he had won among his own folk. Lads better grounded in education than he gathered round him in an eager group and argued into the night. He had a way of cleaving through their doubts. One of them would express, perhaps, a hesitation at offering Christianity in some particular place. Sung-min would look at him in astonishment. Hesitancy? How could there be any? There simply were no arguments against the Christian Way. His rustic simplicity could be seen changing into sublime confidence which had roots in the soil. Its earthy strength fortified the minds of those from gentler backgrounds. He came again and again to these three weeks' schools to study the Christian system of thought and the techniques which expressed it in action. Medicine chest, adult education, co-operative societies, ways of recreation, one by one he wrestled with them. In each school he showed the same pattern; no one found the process of learning more strenuous than he, no one saw the point of learning more clearly; and so he managed to keep abreast of faster minds. He was, his teachers thought, on the border-line between God's skilled mechanics and His navvies. Absurdly enough, it was the navvy peeping out from behind the skills he mastered so painfully which moved people's hearts.

The northern sector of the county was still deeply infiltrated by Communist forces. Its villages had suffered most and their revival lagged behind the rest because of persistent Communist raids. The pre-war group of churches in the area had been almost obliterated. The little market town had in it a derelict house which had been a church, but not more than half a dozen people came to it, and they cautiously and infrequently.

The way opened for this house to be reconstructed. Who should go there and attempt to rebuild? To bring in a trained preacher from some other county would have been to expose him to impossible danger. Any day Communist troops might raid the town and an outsider would have received short shrift from them. In a church not far away one preacher had been left by the raiders suspended from the church's roof-beam by his thumbs.

Sung-min's friend, the preacher in his own county, proposed that the lad should leave his farm and become a full-time preacher. He pointed out that a hill-track, known only to a handful of people, ran from the little town through empty hills and remote valleys back to Sung-min's home. If war-storms arose, there was this way out.

Sung-min moved in, with his medicine chest, his adult school primers and a twist of cotton containing a few clothes. His wife, too, left their home and pattered along the road into danger in his footprints. So he crossed the rubicon and became a full-time servant of the Church. There was that fortuity about the whole business which is often the seal of the Holy Spirit's activities behind human planning.

Round him now curled the little street of twenty shops;

to the north the red hills lowered menacingly. It was all his own peculiar trust, all his to win for Christ. And in the last resort—as his Master, in His day, had the route across the Jordan into the territory of Philip when His enemies pressed too hard—the young couple had their 'sheep run' back to the garrisoned west country.

From the first he took his own line. The repairs to the premises bored him. The chaos of decay did not worry him. The missionary on his first visit found the two eating breakfast in a tiny kitchen, crouched cheerily by the stove with their rice bowls in their hands. The upper floor of the house was being converted into a chapel, and Sung-min had no idea of form or beauty for this room. The arrangements were inelegant, crowded and irritating. The truth was he was seldom at home.

The missionary's second visit was at Sung-min's request. Would his friend come out and see something interesting? Typically, the message was entrusted verbally to a passing coolie. He led the missionary through the little town and headed northward nearer and nearer to the Communist territory but off the main road, stumbling through tenuous rifts between the hills. They passed through a narrow defile and there before them lay a peaceful hamlet, its farms encircling a pond and its land mounting in orderly terraces smiling with green rice. Each house was intact and there was not even a propaganda poster of either party to speak of the war.

"However did you stumble on this?"

" I was wandering round and met a man," replied Sung-min. "I thought you ought to know him."

The man was a neat, quiet fellow. His hamlet, he said,

wanted Christian worship and a night school. The place would provide the furniture and light. He was sure that the Venerable Father of Heaven had guarded them from war and they wanted to worship Him properly. The man had clearly passed through the Sung-min process.

This was but the first of the new preacher's discoveries. The west country preacher's genius for smelling out lapsed Christians became in his apprentice's work a capacity for pin-pointing quiet, thoughtful persons whom God had prepared to listen. In the town he did but little—which annoyed the missionary considerably—his fingers were always probing after the hidden people. Three night schools sprang up, a women's co-operative society to spin cotton, cottage prayer meetings. The chapel on the street of the town at last began to change, for these hidden folk came to it each Sunday and a few street dwellers found courage to join them.

About the time of Europe's Munich, the Japanese ended that. Three times Sung-min and his wife had had to flee before Communist raids, once up their secret road home and twice to new hiding places Sung-min had found. " They move south," he would say, " and we move north." He called this the technique of the mouse hiding under the cat's belly. It was part of his duty and he could cope with raids. When the Japanese aeroplanes swooped on the town and piled its streets with dead, the chapel shared the fate of the town and became a ruin in a deserted place. Sung-min could do nothing about that.

Ten miles away at the mission centre the missionary was in trouble too. The Japanese line ran across the hills a few miles north of the county town and panic, following heavy bombing, drove out the Mission's hospital staff with the town's leaders and influential people. The town was without a government and the hospital without a doctor. Then, miraculously, the Chinese line held, the Japanese were halted, and the poorer folk began to drift back into the town to put up stalls and booths and carry on their trade. The air raids went on and the toll of wounded mounted each day. There were injured men from the line and, in addition, troops defeated farther eastward streamed through the town in disorder. There was a nightmare of need and sorrow in which the hospital was useless for lack of staff.

Two girl-nurses and one probationer came back from the hills and volunteered to reopen the hospital. The missionary ordered Sung-min to send his family home and come to the hospital to protect these workers. He knew that should there be a sudden Japanese break-through, the young man could spirit the girls away. Only this knowledge gave him courage to permit the girls to reopen the work.

He came, like a livening gale of wind, laughing and strong. He declared he would not be content to play 'eunuch' to a nurse's 'dowager empress'; he wanted daily work. He soon found it. The town church had been halved by a bomb-hit and was one of a tangle of half-destroyed buildings which once had been a lovely street. Shutters and doors gaped open; every corner down the whole length of the street housed weary and sick soldiers. They prowled, they scraped for food, they died of cold where they slept.

The church was patched up to serve as a wayside clinic so that masses of soldiers should not be seen from the air to be crowding round the hospital—which so far had escaped bombing. In the morning, when raids were most likely, the staff worked under the Geneva flag in the hospital; as the afternoon wore on, they went to the chapel and treated ulcers, wounds, frost-bite—waited for by a queue which seemed endless. The men were soon found to be lousy and many of them in addition were tormented by scabies. (They had fought in every battle for a year without rest.)

Sung-min discovered his job. The missionary constructed a field fumigation plant for the uniforms and begged from the Red Cross a barrel of sulphur ointment. "I am officer commanding lice and the destruction of the scabies mite," declared Sung-min. To help him, he had a young Welsh missionary recruit who had arrived just in time to share China's war. This strangely assorted pair did their work while the rest dressed wounds in the chapel.

They boiled up great cauldrons of water to bathe the men. As one man soaped himself, blessing God for the gracious lather, they each scrubbed another till he bled. As they scrubbed they harangued each other, each in his own tongue and roaring with laughter; though they could not understand a word, each knew what the other meant. Then came the sulphur process. They scorned the senior nurse's cautions and larded their patients from stem to stern with the ointment, rubbing it in deeply with their own hands. Finally, the fumigator was opened and the cooked clothes restored to their owners.

It went on hour after hour, absurd, grotesque, splendid. Above their heads the shattered roof-beams of the House of God stabbed the evening sky; all round lay wrecked pews, propped to support still lamer men; under their feet the floor was treacherous with soapsuds and the air was choking with charcoal fumes. Naked men stood by the fires, slapped their bare stomachs, stretched their freed limbs, and bawled comments at the Welshman in a language he could not follow. It was quite mad, but with the heavenly sanity which makes one the hills of Han and the Rhondda valley and sweeps in St. Francis's Portiuncula from Italian Umbria to make good measure.

Many divine persistencies stood out in those days, not least that with which the Church carried on its work of training young men for the ministry and young women to be deaconesses. It was sheer service—such as anointing soldiers and fending off disbanded ruffians from the party of nurses threading its way through the wild streets—which led to Way Sung-min being sent for this higher training. The clever can always be trained, the loyal are always worth training.

He went south, with the war on his heels, to the theological seminary. He struggled with the curriculum there as he had in the local training schools and came away with a reputation for sublime cooking. War closed the seminary; he trekked and completed his training in an emergency school. Meanwhile, his wife, away back home, lived a hunted life with her family and his. Now they were at home, now living in bivouacs in the hills to avoid danger.

God, like a rifleman shooting home the bolt of His weapon just before the target flicks into sight, took Sung-min and stationed him where years before the aristocratic Ko Tien-wu had ruled the church and trained the missionary who first selected Way Sung-min. The farm lad followed the imperial officer: when God does things like that it is time to look out for new crises.

The war years had not been kind to the old warrior's churches. The town church, to which Preacher Way went, was tired and in poor heart. Mr Ko's ancestral home in the walled city, which he had bequeathed as a chapel, had fallen into the hands of a quaint sect. The civil war between Nationalist and Communist China loomed grimly over the town's trade. Anything might happen. Sung-min patiently gathered the people around him, not by his preaching, which was never mighty, but by tireless visiting and private talks. He won sectarians into wider fellowship; he unfroze the icy fears that gripped folks' hearts. It is doubtful whether any one of the revivified members would have given Sung-min or his wife the credit for the new cheer which warmed their fellowship; it all happened so quietly that things simply were different.

Difficulties changed Sung-min's work again. His missionary colleague was confronted by a problem which his forerunners had also faced in their days. In the southernmost corner of the wide territory, twenty-five miles from town and in difficult country, there stood a chapel, built on family land, by local money and labour. It belonged to a family whose ancestors had been highwaymen and marauders for centuries. In years gone by they had lived by descending from their fastness to ravage the road along which opium was carried into Central China. One of the last generation had discovered Christianity on a pilgrimage to Nan Yo-shan (the Sacred Mountain) and had won a following in his home.

The first years of Christian development had been full

of thrill very like the first days at Sung-min's own home. Things had changed since then. A clan which had been anti-social for generations could not easily be won into the wide and open Christian fellowship. They were arrogant, aloof, suspicious. Their preacher was one of the clan who tilled his land and lived in his home, sharing their segregation. The church's development stuck for lack of wide fellowship and fresh ideas. Their own hill rampart became a spiritual barrier. Every attempt was passionately resisted. It had been done once, twenty years before Sung-min's day, and the man sent had failed.

Another attempt was now made, and Sung-min was sent to relieve the clan preacher. He came to a clan as tightly knit as his own, but of different name and vastly different tradition. To live there at all, he and his wife had to cramp themselves into one upper room originally built to house the missionary for an occasional night. He patiently set to work to woo the old people and the middle aged—there were no young—of this arrested church. His own experience stood him in good stead. Once more he prodded into the little hamlets and once more sat in little circles round the smoking fires. Younger folks began to drop in to see him. The place revived a little, and best testimony of all, the displaced preacher worked contentedly and well in his tough corner. Sung-min did not know it, God did, but the real inwardness of that stay lay rather in what happened inside Sung-min than what happened in the people for whom he laboured. He learned one more way of living under suspicion and half-enmity.

The nation-wide storm-clouds brought him back to

town. The whole country was seething with change. Day after day saw new triumphs of the Communist arms. The end was drawing near and all knew it. Among the people of the streets excitement was rising, rumours flew and the left element became open in its criticism of the Government and in praise of the new-deal which they prophesied was coming with the invading forces. As years before he had been called out to service by a missionary needing a man to face peril, so now, another, looking for one on whom he could rely, called Way Sung-min back to stand with him to share the unknown red starlight.

He returned to a town of wild delirium; the new Government was in. The drums were beating and the firecrackers barking as he shouldered his way back to the central church. The guilds were out in the streets in monstrous processions. The unions had their banners flying; the people, marching by their trades, carried implements and symbols proclaiming their allegiance to the new People's Government. They were shepherded by Communist troops and led by the blue-uniformed workers of the Party. Men on tall stilts danced in mad career up and down the long line which filled the street.

Everything swiftly turned over to meet the new era. The old officials disappeared and new young men, intent and severe, took their places. The old currency was scrapped and the new flooded the shops. The people were so eager that this new currency remained buoyant and gave the first testimony of stability. Everywhere, however, the work of security was quietly pushed home in house and shop and organization. This home was inviolate, that suspect; this organization permitted, that proscribed. Sudden death came here and elevation to power there.

This time there could be no retreat back into the terrritories of another government. The time of Way Sung-min's full testing was come. The Christian Church stood out, too big to hide, too well-known to ignore, and with its international connections proclaimed by the presence of foreigners. It could not hope to escape the attention of the new regime. In its organization Sung-min stood out as a leader, trained by his years of adventurous service, hardened by privations and born with the sounds of civil strife about his mother's ears, he was at last where God had meant, so long before, that he should be. In every society when a new rule comes to China, someone must, as the people phrase it, " stick out his head ". Sung-min was brought there, and knew it, to stick out his head.

God had groomed the lad, now grown man, for the task. In his full strength, the son of the soil who had loved and served the common folk so long and so well, was confident with the experience of many escapes, and so deeply initiated into the ways of the toiling farm and working people that the proletarian vigour of People's Government could not scare him. Mr Ko had fitted this place when the trailing clouds of the old imperialism still held prestige; he was now dead and was replaced by one as fitted to the new as the old man had been to the past.

Elsewhere, Christian leaders with a landowner or moneyed background went to prison. No one could tell when Mr Way's turn would come, but it was very hard to pick out of that life anything on which to pin a charge—

very difficult except at one point; he loved his foreign colleagues.

The first test came from another angle. It was part of the results of the spying upon the activities of people's movements. A Communist bureau moved into part of his church's premises and its staff therefore lived side by side with the church workers. In this way, the new zealots could observe that prayer meetings, classes and visits went on uninterruptedly. Previously, troops and others who had billeted themselves upon the church were content to use the property. Times were now changed, and the new occupiers could not tolerate any unofficial teaching of the people.

The Communist Manifesto, however, had proclaimed freedom of religion, and the attack had to be made obliquely. Posters and slogans, newspapers and speeches, were joined in one great cry, *Sheng tsan,* ' produce material results '—create wealth. This was described as the citizen's foremost duty. Polite but firm police officers informed the leaders of the Church that they were wasting the people's time. They should not be gathered in classes of instruction but out at work producing something which could be eaten, worn or used. Classes, they said, must cease forthwith. It is so that a faith can be proscribed without proscribing it.

Mr Way took the long journey down the winding street alone to interview the chief of police. This was sticking his head out indeed. Gently he reminded the chief of the clauses about religion in the leader's manifesto. His people, he explained, were only employing their leisure in ways to make them more efficient in the service of man.

They did not gather to gamble, smoke opium or plot reaction. They found that the study of Marx, which was compulsory, made them think, and that the study of Christianity's Carpenter made them strong to do. For this once, he won and the order was withdrawn.

Here and there over the country, however, the net of the new ideology tightened and the Christian leaders were involved in trouble. Some were hailed before people's courts on charges laid by persons who had been passed over by the previous government or the wartime relief authorities. These now came forward to testify that the Christians in custody had administered war relief and lined their own pockets. Yesterday's good deeds could easily be a man's undoing, for in some people's eyes a thing is only good if done under the orthodox auspices.

Each day whispered in Sung-min's ear that a man cannot bear a charmed life for ever. The final assault might come from any angle; there was need for all round defence day and night. The process of impeachment is so easy; the deployment of defensive evidence so hard. Mission property is well built: men may covet it; a preacher's personal contacts are so wide: one forgotten interview of months before could suddenly confront him with accusation. Others had gone before, both Chinese and foreign: their mistakes remembered now could cost his head. The Church membership is wide: a flaw in the record of one member could bring him to the courts.

Like Jesus' good householder, Sung-min brought from his stores of experience things new and old. His knowledge of the Communist outlook, absorbed in his youth, his ear for rumour, tuned in the war, his intuitive sense of what was passing in the mind of labourer and shopkeeper, acquired in a thousand fireside talks, his mobility and habit of judging what to say from listening to the trailing ends of conversation, his habituation to resistance—these were his lifeline. He picked his way carefully through the first days of the new era with that goat-footed sureness with which he skipped among the rocks and hills of his home.

One dangerous habit could not be cured in him and was built into his life as surely as the things which protected him. His dogged loyalty to his Western colleagues could not be rooted out. He owed them so much, they were so much part of his Christian world of thought, that to ostracize them or politely find himself too engaged to meet them proved impossible.

Of all the peculiarities of the Christian Church in the new world, however, this possession of Western staff towered above the rest in blatant anomaly. The regime as it settled into its stride became more and more suspicious of these foreigners. Mr Ko often found his missionary colleagues useful tools: in Mr Way's world the contrary was the case. The Christians had to explain away the presence of these persons "tainted with imperialist Western thinking". Persons who had been friends down long years quietly disappeared, calling no more. Communist friends of Christians continually pressed upon them the fact that toleration of Christianity meant the toleration of Chinese Christianity not "reactionary agents".

Sung-min was right in the thick of this criticism, hearing it every day, but he would not cease his visits and counsels with his colleagues. He knew that the missionary's presence was now an embarrassment to the struggling church but the cords of love bound him too fast to admit it.

As anti-foreignism grew, the missionary had to give the last help he could and cut the knot which Sung-min's fingers would not untie. He prised loose the clasp of those loyal hands and made ready to leave. So, for the last time, a boat prepared to drop downstream, bearing foreign passengers to the wide world outside. This time there was no tier of bunks cheerily shared between the Chinese and foreign band of friends. Sung-min arranged for the boat and stood alone on the bank to watch it drop down to the turn of the river.

He was afraid with a strange uprooting fear he had never felt before. The newness of the new world without the old system of help and colleagueship daunted even his bright spirit. Where the river twists out of sight below the town, there stands a pagoda which for years has braved every wind of heaven. Sung-min felt that he was left to stand there as exposed as that symbol of a bygone religion. A dreadful loneliness swept across his mind, but he treasured a thousand memories which will haunt his dreams. They parted on the Christian blessing, "God's peace upon your path. We shall meet again."

He turned from the river bank as the boat passed from sight, turned to face the red starlight alone, heir to the future.

Daily on the wings of prayer his cries for help, counsel and guidance wing their way across the bamboo curtain and are caught in the hearts of those who love him here in the 'imperialist West'. Nightly their prayers return. There is no blockade-runner to compare with God.

91

. . . *What then shall we say to these things? If God is for us, who is against us? . . . Nay, in all these things we are more than conquerors through Him that loved us.*

Is this
the Beginning?

THE Chinese Communist Party has travelled a long road, strewn with the bodies of enthusiasts, to gain control of the nation. The Party's history goes back to the year 1920. It is an epic story of determination, sometimes written within the history of the other revolutionary parties, sometimes diverging from it violently.

The way has been marked by towering landmarks. There is the bitter siege in the fastnesses of Central China to record: there is the fantastic march to the new area in the north. The records of the Eighth and Fourth Route Armies in their resistance to aggression will live for years in the nation's memory. It is hard to believe it now, but there was a day when American news reporters praised this movement and American generals congratulated the very men who now stand opposed in stiff-necked non-co-operation against all that is Anglo-American. The world may forget but the Chinese schoolboy, now going up to university, remembers that these Communist troops fashioned artillery from tree-trunks and hollowed out great stones to make land mines. These things, whether we like them or hate them, are part of the story.

The Christian can easily miss the direction in which the Finger of God points if he is captured by the scream of popular newspapers and is not prepared to look at the story of Communism in China with dispassionate eyes. He can never hope to share in the life the Chinese Christian must live behind the bamboo curtain unless he faces and attempts to interpret the meaning of the Communist struggle.

The Communist movement in China is part of the folk-change of history. It takes its place beside the imperialist campaigns of Nineveh and Babylon recorded in the Old Testament. In the Bible story the revelation of the Divine Will and the shaping of the Chosen People was effected by the pressures of these great powers. The Bible shows us the prophets looking eagerly at these crises and by inspired intuition, striking out of them flashes of meaning, Divine meaning.

Our God is a God of history, alive and active. The people's movements of Eastern Asia, including the changes

94

in China are inside God's world. God speaks in them; would that all the Lord's people were prophets.

There is no doubt that the welcome afforded to the People's Democracy by the Chinese people was given in the sincere belief that with its coming "judgment would roll down as waters and righteousness as a mighty stream" across a land sickened by corruption and self-seeking. Whether justice will roll through the land or not is beside the point, the point is that the Chinese heart ached because of social sin and welcomed catastrophe to end the sin. "It cannot be worse," they said.

The Bible student can appreciate the things for which the Chinese nation longs. They are the basic qualities of moral society, honest taxation, uncorrupt officials, fair land tenure, open markets. These are the things for which the Prophets thundered in Israel and Judah. From Amos to Malachi, the prophets insisted that it was the absence of these qualities in the nation which brought down upon it the blows of the great powers. Their voices are joined by the voices of the Chinese sages. To the modern man in the Chinese tea-shop, good government and social honesty appear so lovely that he is prepared to accept them from any source, and the party that brings them can have his loyalty, not only for them but for its whole programme.

Whether, in fact, the inception of Communist government means that at last these basic virtues are to become part of Chinese social life, only the years can tell. The peasant and shopkeeper are content to wait and watch— and no one in the world can watch more keenly than they. If what they see is the real thing, then this Chinese government will be to them what Babylonian government became to Nehemiah and Ezra, an alien but beneficent power meriting support.

So far the record is quite good. There has been honest taxation, heavy, clumsy, painful, but honest. There has been simple, rough justice from officials. Great men have moved among the common folk, clad as they are clad and fed as they are fed. Privilege has been attacked, legislation has been keyed up to fill empty stomachs. The smokescreen of verbiage that concealed inefficiency has been blown away and the new leaders have humbly sought help in administration. If the movement continues in this way, the whole programme of the Communist Party will be underwritten by the people and it will remain. The expansion into neighbouring territories, alignment with the Eastern bloc and hostility to Western 'interference' in China will become a national programme. Bloodbaths may be tolerated. These things will be to the citizen simply the coin with which he buys internal order.

There is the other side to the picture. The materialism which is inherent in modern Communism will spread across the nation. The things which we abhor in modern Communism—police surveillance, dragooning of thought, psychological pressure on minority groups, the splitting of God's one world into two artificial camps, the contempt for religion—these, too, will become part of the accepted pattern of daily life until a generation grows up which remembers nothing else. The tragedy of the Jews who grew fond of Babylon and would not return will be re-enacted on a vaster scale.

The pressure of this changing temper has, so far, fallen heaviest upon the missionary staff working within the

Chinese Church. Many have already left the China scene and all seem destined to disappear. Indeed, their disappearance seems to be the condition upon which the Church can remain. The cry, so widespread as to appear officially inspired, is, " Christianity? Yes. This we may manage to tolerate, at least temporarily, for it has social conscience, but foreign agents of international Christianity, definitely no ! "

The general hostility against the West, with its characteristic suspicious fear, has found its easiest mark in the missionary force. This has always been so in the waves of xenophobia which accompany China's tragic struggles.

The pressure has also fallen at other points. Under the drive to achieve totality in the control of thought, the great network of hospitals, schools, universities and institutions operated by the Christian movement has begun to be absorbed into the national system and removed from church control. This process is being accelerated every month. The attack also aims at severing the links with the Western churches out of which the various parts of the Chinese Church have sprung. Through the mouths of agents, supporters and ' well wishers ', the Christians have been shown that though religion is tolerated, it must be religion in territorial units and not in world association streams. Christianity must retire behind the curtain, safe from imperialist contamination.

Even the internal, devotional life of the simple churches has come under pressure. Programmes of religious life are subjected to inspection. Leaders are vigorously catechized. Bible study groups have been closed down on the grounds that people should be at work producing food or goods, not studying a religion which produces no bread. All this is done in the green tree; what shall be done in the dry?

What can the world Christian think about the China he has loved? There is so much in this picture which is horrible to him that if he simply looks upon its surface he may well despair of rescuing anything out of the revolution. It is different if we look more deeply. Both the Bible and the subsequent history of Christian expansion teach us that when there is a great stirring of the people, and nations are on the march from the old to something new, there is always a parallel change inside the Church.

The stir within the Church always moves along a line which, at some point, converges with the secular movement. This is God's dialectical process and it runs at a deeper level than the Marxist. It is spiritual. In times of the making and breaking of nations, Christian history itself warns us to look closely at the Church of God. A new thing is certain to emerge from it.

This being so, can we trace that converging line? The answer surely is that the pioneer activities of the earlier missionaries blossomed out into two things—an institutional drive to capture the nation for Christ, particularly its young intelligentsia, and the birth of a self-conscious Church in place of the old 'Mission'. The Edinburgh Missionary Conference of 1910 marks a period in these two Christian movements which correlates with the birth of the Communist movement in China in the second decade of the century, though both have earlier foreshadowings.

In hospitals, training centres, and in hundreds of smaller schools, devoted Western Christians were brought

98

into the closest contact with keen young Chinese who drank in from their teachers a discontent with the old China and a deep conviction that renewal and Christianity were tied together. Often the motives which moved these young people to study their Western friends were national and social. Christianity thus threw a ferment into the life of China. Part of the Chinese thirst for social righteousness was implanted by missionary work. It grew out beyond the borders of the Church, and even now some of the social urge which energizes Communism is a ' garden escape' from missionary compounds. Communist toleration of religion is partly explained by the Church's social record.

These things could not happen without being reflected in Church life itself. The incoming of trained Chinese met the keen welcome and deep desire of the missionaries to create a Chinese Christian Church in which Western-centred organization operated by foreign missionaries should be replaced by a Chinese organization controlled and staffed by Chinese Christians. So Chinese leadership grew up alongside Western, and at last, especially in institutions, superseded it. Architecture, finance, authorship, hymn-writing, art and liturgy all mark this change-over.

So an era dawned in which Western Christians, in the widest coverage of foreign people China has ever known, lived intimately with her people in cities and in villages, sharing life in the deep things and the lesser in such a way that there has been a community of the spirit for years. While the Communist motto for twenty-five years has been ' struggle' the Christian motto has been ' fellowship', fellowship in identification with the people's needs, fellow-

99

ship at the deep spiritual levels which are only open to religious people. The magnificent roll of Chinese bishops and other Church leaders testifies to the efficacy of this way of shared life.

This deep interpenetration of spirit between those of the older Church and the emerging Church is of great significance now that we have reached the cross-roads in history. If we take our clue from the Old Testament and acknowledge that in the great revolutionary movements of China during the last hundred years, God, the Living Lord of history, has been at work making a gigantic wall-poster such as is to be seen dominating Hankow or the Red Square—throwing on paint in mighty splashes—this work has not exhausted His labours. He is never engaged only on one task. He has simultaneously been painting His miniatures, limning in with infinite delicacy the personal characteristics of individual people. It is no surprise to people brought up on the Bible to discover that the key to the whole of God's work lies in the miniatures. After all, a Middle Eastern famine produced a Joseph and the incursions of a powerful nation threw up King David.

To the non-Christian, it might appear absurd to equate the changes we can see in, say, the life of one girl nurse with the march of the Red Army from Central China to the west and north. In the world as God is ruling it, it is not absurdity but the very pith of reality. It rings with the same authenticity as made one Carpenter nailed upon a Roman cross the watershed of history. He has eternal significance, and Rome, Jewry and Grecian culture had temporal significance which served as foil to show His meaning.

100

In the same way, within the gigantic military and political upheaval of China's life, there is only one thing which, despite appearances, is eternal. It is the Church of God. All change exists to further the growth of this Divine Society.

Here the lines of national revolution and Church life converge. The social revolution has reached the point of Communist dominance and at that point comes the moment in which the missionaries from the non-Communist world are thrust out of China. At this point also the institutional tools of the missionary movement are gathered in by the ruling government. God is not bewildered by this moment. Long before it happened He had prepared for the continuance of the thing most precious to Him, the life of His Church.

This is why the portraits in this book are cogent. These are the miniatures which give the clue to God's mighty acts. They are alike crucial for the Church and the Nation. They are directly important for the Church because they are portraits of the rank and file of God's people in China upon whom now rests the whole responsibility for the welfare of the Church. They are ultimately crucial for the whole Chinese Nation because the health of the Church within it is the criterion by which God judges every civilization. Herod and his puppet kingdom were judged by Jesus wearing the purple robe of scorn; Agrippa by a prison-sick Paul wan for lack of sunlight. Communist China will be judged at the Highest Tribunal by what happens to these simple folk, for their simplicity masks the fact that they are God's people.

They are simple people, not one of the great Chinese

101

Christian leaders is among them. This is because under a Communist regime more than any other it is the common man who is the test. Leaders are often muzzled, throttled, silenced. The common man in the lanes and byways is the person who survives to think and act. Leaders in all nations can be exceptional, running far ahead of the mass in achievement. The most important thing in first century Christianity was the quality of life of the people who are listed in the last pages of Paul's letters.

Can people who are mature in Christianity look at the five persons portrayed in this book, knowing they are typical of hundreds, and say, " I know that face; it bears the characteristics of Jesus?" We can be sure that the son of the Mother in Israel will bear as long as he lives the hall-mark of Jesus. We recognize something which belongs to no nation but is peculiarly Christian in the hard-won humility of the Chinese nurse. It is the redeemed proletariat that we see in Mr Way. Those who went before have infected these people with their own experience of Jesus. Many Westerners who will never see China again have left bits of their best selves inside these folk who are the Church of tomorrow.

It looks as if that Church of tomorrow will be stripped of its great institutional expressions and be simply the worshipping community in towns and villages. It will in this only parallel the Church of the West. It will grow, a people's movement within a People's Democracy, and grow around such people as are sketched here. Such persons as these will fight a good fight. By compromise and alignment when they are possible, by ardent love of the people at all times and, if necessary, by the path of

Stephen, they will express the essential Faith in terms fitted to the world into which God has brought them.

Could this result of a Chinese Church witnessing in simplicity to a Chinese people have been brought about in any other way? Had there to be this violent stripping down? Could not the enterprise have evolved gently from subsidy to self-support, from foreign dominance to foreign participation, all peacefully and sweetly? Many would answer, yes. Tremendous effort, thought and prayer has been spent on making the Church really Chinese by constitutional change. The revolution has swept across a process which has gone on for years.

Some would answer the question saying, no. What parent has ever found it easy to yield full autonomy to his growing child? What mother has ever kept her finger right out of her son's marriage?

It has happened this way; speculation on what might have been is pointless; it can also be blasphemous. It would be as easy to rewrite the Bible as this page in Chinese history. It is sound religion to stand astonished and acknowledge the hand of the Lord. This is not the first time the Kingdom has suffered violence. We must have the courage to watch the Chinese Christian Church pass behind the curtain into the red starlight, determined to follow it with prevailing prayer and every gift that it is still able to receive.

It is also our duty, and the Chinese leaders would be the first to point it out, to receive the Word of God concerning other areas of the world in which we can still labour. We must see that with all haste and with everything that can possibly be done we raise up national men

103

and women fit to lead the Church and be the Church when the doors close upon us there too. While it is day, we must live with the people of the younger churches until the things we live by are part of them. Not in China only, the night cometh in which no man may work. Time presses in every field.

This is the meaning of the portent of the twelve-pointed Sun of Nationalist China sinking in the China Sea. This is the prophecy of the Star and the Cross in conjunction over China. Let him that readeth understand. God has brought us to a beginning.